LEARN TO TEACH

# Meditation and Mindfulness

## A COMPREHENSIVE GUIDE AND SCRIPTING FOR MEDITATION TEACHERS

S.G. MCKEEVER

ISBN: 978-1-885479-06-8

Editing by Astika Mason, Delaney Patterson
Cover design by Banalata Sundquist
Book formatting by Nicole Sturk

Printed in the United States of America
First printing August 2021

For additional information contact:
McKeever Publishing
P.O. Box 161167
San Diego, CA 92176

SAN DIEGO   SAN FRANCISCO   FAIRFAX

# CONTENTS

**CHAPTER 1: TEACHING A GUIDED MEDITATION**      1

Sharing Your Inspiration      1

Some Frequent Questions      4

Public Speaking      6

Engaging the Senses      7

Setting Goals      9

**CHAPTER 2: BECOMING A MEDITATION TEACHER**      11

Being a Mentor      12

Offering Guidance      14

Inspire!      16

**CHAPTER 3: PREPARING FOR CLASS**      19

Plan Ahead      20

Your Appearance      21

Arrive Early      21

Atmospherics      22

Props and Materials      23

Music      24

Greeting Your Audience      24

Refreshments and Sales      25

## CHAPTER 4: A TYPICAL MEDITATION CLASS — 27

The Class Outline — 27

Your Introduction and Program Overview — 28

Engage Your Audience — 30

*Icebreaker* — *31*

Discuss Meditation and Mindfulness — 32

*Analogies* — *33*

*The Science* — *37*

Guide the Meditation Experience — 38

*Voice and Verbiage* — *38*

*Posture* — *39*

*Using Breath to Establish Flow* — *40*

*Part 1: Energizing Exercise* — *41*

*Part 2: Conscious Relaxation* — *42*

*Part 3: Concentration Exercise* — *42*

*Part 4.1: Guided Visualizations* — *45*

*Part 4.2: Meditation* — *47*

*Part 5: Assimilation and Manifestation* — *48*

Ending Class and Next Steps — 49

## CHAPTER 5: TEACHING MEDITATION TO CHILDREN — 51

Childhood Stress — 52

How to Choose Meditation Techniques for Children — 54

Stages of Development — 55

Integrating Meditation into Scholastic Activities — 56

*Science* — *57*

*Math* — *58*

*Language Arts* — *58*

*History* — *58*

Conclusion — 59

# Contents

**CHAPTER 6: THE SUN OF AWARENESS**     **61**

Explanation for the Sun of Awareness     61

**CHAPTER 7: CLASS SCRIPTS**     **65**

Orchestrating an IceBreaker     66

Part 1: Energizing Exercise     67

Part 2: Conscious Relaxation Exercises     69

*A Preliminary Breathing Exercise*     69

*Conscious Relaxation*     70

*The Body Scan Exercise*     72

Part 3: Concentration Exercises     76

*Concentration on the External Senses*     77

*Concentration on the Heartbeat and Pulses in the Body*     78

*Concentration on the Internal Senses*     78

*Concentration on Breath Awareness*     80

Part 4: Guided Visualizations and Meditations     82

*Visualization Scripts*     84

*Heart Center Meditation*     86

*Tune and Brighten the Mind*     87

*Shift to Focus on Sensation*     88

*The Observer and the Observed*     90

*Chanting Mantra and Japa*     96

*Meditation on Fun*     100

*Mindful Movement and Walking Meditation*     101

*Loving-Kindness Meditation*     103

*Mindful Eating*     108

*Concluding The Meditation*     109

Part 5: Assimilation and Manifestation     110

    *Assimilation Exercise*     *110*

Ending Class and Next Steps     110

**CHAPTER 8: THE SCIENCE OF MEDITATION**     **113**

The Autonomic Nervous System and the Body's Stress
Response     113

Modern Stress     114

Understanding Our Nervous System     115

How To Activate the Parasympathetic Nervous System     117

**ADDITIONAL READING**     **121**

## CHAPTER 1

# Teaching a Guided Meditation

## SHARING YOUR INSPIRATION

*"What lies behind us and what lies before us are tiny matters compared to what lies within us."*

—RALPH WALDO EMERSON

The time-honored activity of meditation is an experience unlike any other. A deeply personal pursuit, whether carried out in solitude or in a group setting, and sometimes led by a guide, the practice of meditation can have profoundly positive effects on the quality of one's life. The experience of meditation—and the mindfulness it engenders—can relieve the tensions and strains of everyday life, promote mental and emotional clarity, generate feelings of purpose and meaning, give rise to personal empowerment, kindle inspiration and creativity, and provide support during challenging situations and major life transitions, to name a few.

The ability to *teach* meditation to others is a powerful gift that, when shared, can set in motion the transformation of lives of others. Sharing the meditation experience can also elevate your personal feelings of joy and fulfillment. I have found teaching meditation to be one of the most satisfying experiences of my life.

Interested in meditation and spirituality since I was a young child, I have studied meditation formally for thirty years, both with the guidance of teachers and as an individual seeker. It's my honor to offer this guide to those of you wishing to share meditation with others.

I have taught meditation to thousands of people in countries around the world and have developed a teaching format that is concise and effective. It encompasses offering a class overview, introducing myself, and giving the audience a framework through which to understand meditation. The framework varies according to the audience but typically includes the following: energy exercises, conscious relaxation, concentration, guided visualizations, meditation, assimilation, manifestation, and next steps.

Some of you will use this guide to share meditation with others casually; others will want to delve more deeply into the art and science of meditation so you can teach it to others on a regular professional basis. In either case, you will be doing a service by helping generate clarity, peace, harmony, and mindfulness among your friends, family, and community. In this book, you will learn the skills required to share meditation with one person or with a large audience.

A note on the terms *mindfulness* and *meditation*: in this book they are used interchangeably. While *mindfulness* is an intentional awareness of what is happening in the present moment in one's mind, body, and environment, *meditation* is a practice that fosters mindfulness. In this sense, mindfulness is a state of awareness achieved through the practice of meditation.

Meditation instruction is often blended into programs focusing on study areas such as yoga, stress and anxiety mitigation, corporate wellness, and sports training. In such programs, there may not be an experienced meditation instructor on hand. The good news is that you don't have to be an advanced meditator to guide an audience in meditation. Even if you don't meditate yourself, you can guide a meditation class, simply by following the scripts in this book. The scripts provided in chapter 7 of this book will give you the tools to lead a variety of exercises.

The keys to teaching meditation are a heartfelt desire to help others and a genuine enthusiasm for your subject matter. Your sincerity as a teacher is the inner glow that will illuminate your own path and the path upon which you guide others. Furthermore, the inspiration you find in your own practice of meditation will help you inspire others in theirs. Your enthusiasm for sharing the practice will be felt and appreciated by your audience as they begin to participate in the uplifting experience that is meditation.

That said, even with the most earnest interest in helping your audience, it is wise to remain somewhat detached as to how people react to your instruction. Some individuals are not at a stage in their life or personal development where meditation will resonate with them. Give others the freedom to take or leave what you have to offer, and give yourself permission to not be everyone's cup of tea.

## SOME FREQUENT QUESTIONS

**Is meditation associated with religion?** This question may be on the minds of some in your audience, even if the question is not asked. The techniques offered in this book are rooted in a wisdom as old as humanity and therefore universal in their application. All human beings seek inner peace and release from stress and other forms of mental and physical suffering. The methods presented in this book can help people better understand their bodies, minds, and emotions, regardless of their religious beliefs. Furthermore, meditation brings us the quiet time we need to ponder our life's deepest questions. For some, these questions may be religious in nature; for others, not.

**How do yoga and meditation fit together?** Yoga is a formalized system of philosophy and personal development that has existed for thousands of years. Meditation is one of the eight "limbs," or aspects, of yoga. The eight aspects of yoga are traditionally divided into two groups. The first four are considered the *outer* limbs of yoga, which deal with the actions of the physical as expressed in the yogic body and breath exercises. The second four aspects are considered the *inner* limbs of yoga. These deal with exercises of consciousness that turn our attention inward from the physical senses, by way of focused concentration, meditation, and the experience of blissful trance. Meditation is the essence of these inner aspects of yoga.

**What is the science behind the practice of meditation?** There are numerous scientific studies that support the practice of meditation and mindfulness. In chapter 8 of this book, we'll explore some of the science behind meditation. As a teacher, you will want to identify which areas of scientific research apply to your topics of instruction. Mentioning the science that supports meditation will give credibility to your instruction and inspire your audience to dive deeper into their practice. Some first-time practitioners report immediate relief from stress, anxiety, and physical tensions; however, research suggests that those who sustain their practice enjoy increasing and enduring benefits.

## PUBLIC SPEAKING

*"Most people would rather be down in the grave
than giving the eulogy."*

—JERRY SEINFELD

Public speaking is listed by many as one of their greatest fears, but there's no getting around public speaking in the teaching profession. Verbal communication is a primary tool for teachers. Public speaking takes practice, but the practice does not need to be in front of a live audience. You can stand in your living room and practice projecting your voice while enunciating your words, or you can practice in front of a supportive friend or relative.

Often, the fear of public speaking derives from the fear of not being able to memorize a script. Fortunately, an effective meditation class can be guided simply by reading the scripts provided in this book or by reading scripts you have created yourself. Because their eyes will likely be closed during the meditation and their attention turned inward, you won't need to worry about reading to your audience. An audience would rather hear a steady and confident voice as you read from well-conceived note cards than hear you struggle to recite exercises from memory.

Perhaps more than most subjects, teaching meditation requires a calm, clear voice. Audiences will easily comprehend your words when you speak with a relaxed tone and good volume. It's also essential to be as concise as possible in your explanations and analogies.

When engaged in day-to-day speech, we habitually infuse our pauses with fillers such as "uh," "um," and—perhaps the most common of all—"you know." When teaching meditation, try to avoid these even if it feels unnatural at first. Relax into your confidence so your words can work their magic. Your relaxed energy will soothe the audience and promote the peace and relaxation they came for.

In addition to your vocal delivery and relaxed energy, it's good to consider the use of silence in your presentations. Momentary pauses can be very effective. They allow time for your audience to ponder and absorb your words. People need time, space, and silence to move their attention inward into their bodies, breath, and minds. Give them that time, space, and quiet.

## ENGAGING THE SENSES

When guiding others in meditation, I suggest referring to all five senses. People experience life through their five senses: sight, sound, touch, taste, and smell, with sight, sound, and touch being the primary senses. Depending on the type of meditation experience, the senses of taste and smell may not always be relevant, but to include these senses you can direct students to be conscious of their tongues and any odors or scents they can discern in the environment.

Each person typically utilizes one primary sense in his or her day-to-day life. This primary sense is used by the person's conscious mind to navigate the world. Interestingly, each person then draws on an alternate sense to access the subconscious mind, and this is the sense used to enter meditation. For example, a sound engineer makes extensive use of hearing in his or her professional life, but when it comes time to relax and journey inward during a meditation class, visualization or kinesthetic exercises may provide a welcome change.

By listening carefully to people, we can often identify a person's primary sense reference. People speak of how a particular event or circumstance *looks*, *feels*, or *sounds* to them. In a single meditation class, there won't be time for this kind of individualized attention, so a good practice is to refer to at least three of the five physical senses when guiding a meditation. Again, the three physical senses most often referenced by the conscious mind are sight, sound, and tactile sensation.

Some examples of sense-based meditation exercises are given below.

♦ Visual: Imagine that your breath is a beautiful golden color. Visualize the breath flowing in and out of your body. Gaze inward and imagine a bright light, the sun, or a candle flame bringing light to your heart.

◆ Auditory: Listen to your body. Tune into the sounds it makes: the whirring of blood and the rhythm of your heartbeat. Acknowledge the internal harmony as you relax and let go of outer sounds and distractions. Enjoy the inner silence.

◆ Tactile or Kinesthetic: As you breathe in, become aware of your bodily feelings and sensations. As you exhale, notice the feelings and sensations stirred by releasing the breath.

◆ Smell: Bring awareness to your nose and nasal cavity. Become aware of any scents or odors in the air.

◆ Taste: Become aware of your tongue. Allow your tongue to sink motionless to the bottom of your mouth. Be aware of any tastes or flavors.

◆ Combining Sensory Images: Imagine a beach with turquoise water (visual), the steady sound of undulating waves (auditory), and the sensation of a coastal breeze as it glides over your skin (touch). Notice the salty scent of the air (smell) and the flavor of ocean spray on your lips (taste).

## SETTING GOALS

In my book *Strategy for Success,* I discuss how to use meditation to establish and achieve goals. Before addressing an audience, it is considerate to have some idea of the audience's motivations and goals. Why have they come to meditate? What are they searching for? If you understand your audience in this way, you will be better equipped to offer them the tools they need to achieve their goals.

Your students are no doubt seeking something: peace of mind, alleviation of social anxiety, like-minded community, the means to deal with an emotional or physical illness or injury, or perhaps a way to dispel grief. As a teacher, it behooves you to be mindful of the audience's reasons for showing up to class. Creating this foundation of aware-ness will help orient you in showing them how meditation can aid them in their journey forward.

The way forward may call for a variety of individually tai-lored solutions, but those solutions will be more effective when grounded in deeper self-knowledge. The essence of meditation is self-knowledge—the discovery of one's own true nature. With that wisdom, action can be directed more effectively.

## CHAPTER 2

# Becoming a
# Meditation Teacher

Before we dive into the classroom techniques and exercises, let me say a few things about the influential role you will be assuming as a meditation instructor.

The most elemental tool for any meditation teacher is the teacher's intention. Intention creates karma, a concept which signifies both the nature of an effort and the results that arise from that effort. Intention is foundational to every action, but it is especially critical in meditation and similar disciplines where the relationship between teacher and student has a profound impact on the efficacy of instruction. Take the time to examine your motives for wanting to teach meditation.

Before beginning each class, take time to set your intention and imagine the results of succeeding in your intention.

## BEING A MENTOR

A teacher of any subject may find themselves in the role of mentor. If you instruct meditation on a regular basis, you may eventually be seen as a mentor by some of your students. The role of mentor brings responsibilities beyond that of dispensing classroom information, so it may be wise to first decide if the role of mentor is one you are comfortable with. If it is, be prepared to assume that role when the occasion arises.

Meditation teachers engage students in a more intimate way than teachers of other subjects. This is due to the deeply personal aspect of spending time in meditation and the trust involved in allowing a guide to lead one there. Some students will want to engage your wisdom and advice outside of the curriculum. They may wish to share their personal stories with you. Naturally, you will want to do your best by the students; however, I strongly advise you to proceed with caution! Unless you are a licensed psychologist or certified life counselor (in which case you should be paid to offer mentoring), you may inadvertently do yourself and your students a disservice by attempting to give advice.

I suggest steering the conversation back to the students' meditation practice and avoiding getting into the specifics of their personal lives. You can't be expected to work out solutions to their life questions. You can, however, as their *meditation teacher*, offer them empowerment through a set of tools. With the tools and with practice, the students may uncover the clarity, wisdom, and insights needed to navigate their personal journeys. This powerful set of tools you offer is enough. Staying clear about your offering will ensure you remain constructive in your role as a meditation instructor and perceived mentor.

It will be good to familiarize yourself with a variety of resources to which a student can be referred: books, coaches, therapists, doctors, spiritual groups, podcasts, and so on. Tap into the network of resources in your community and don't hesitate to make referrals. You will never possess the sum of all the knowledge your students may need, but you can be like a librarian who points to helpful resources.

And remember, you are not only a meditation teacher but also a human being. Don't hesitate to share yourself with your students. (As with above, be sure to keep the conversation centered in meditation.) Meditation is a vast and highly subjective topic that can provide the seeker with a lifetime of intellectual, emotional, and spiritual exploration. Your personal anecdotes may remind them there is always something new to learn or bring to their practice. Share a few sentences on what meditation means for *you* at the start of each class, and then share how your class may help *them* grasp the bigger picture of meditation as a life philosophy and personal practice.

## OFFERING GUIDANCE

Teachers of academic subjects such as history or math are not typically expected to also teach their students how to study, how to engender good study habits, or how to prioritize the knowledge they have taught. You will discover, however, that taking on these wider responsibilities is exactly what meditation teachers do.

Because the practice of meditation does not exist in a vacuum, your students will ideally apply the skills and habits they learn in meditation to their day-to-day lives. If this pragmatic application doesn't happen, your classes won't result in personal growth or real-world results for the students. Pointers from you on how to integrate the effects of their meditation practice into their everyday lives will be much appreciated by your students.

It may take time for you to get to know your students and for them to share their circumstances with you. However, from the very first class, let your students know any plan for practice should include both personal and group meditations and a regular frequency and place for each type. This is a starting point from which a more personalized plan can later emerge.

If designed and executed well, your classes may be the most potent instance for a positive feedback loop to occur, inspiring students to return again and again and thereby experience the long-term effects of a regular practice.

Some students will find it difficult to follow even a simple beginner's plan. Ironically, adding a new activity such as tennis or a new class at school can almost always be done, even by those who are very busy, yet finding time for inner peace and stillness can seem impossible to many. This is because we habitually neglect our inner welfare in favor of outer activities, and, at first, meditation may seem like doing nothing. Few people will make time to do nothing.

Your task as a meditation teacher is to help students learn that meditation is indeed *doing something*, and that *something* can be hugely integral to their wellbeing and success in all their life activities. You can show them that the benefits of meditation do not come from thinking or intellectualizing about meditation but rather from doing it in a regular and reliable way.

You will be called upon to suggest how many times a day, week, or month your students need to practice to reap the benefits, as well as what time of day. They may ask about an appropriate duration—ten minutes, a half-hour, an hour? They may need advice on how to stay focused, how to keep from falling asleep, what to do about back or knee pain, and so on. You can do your best to tailor suggestions to their needs, but encourage your students to be experimental, playful, and flexible in their approach. An eager learner may be turned off by regimens that are too rigid or overbearing.

Leverage your personal experience to help students set realistic and attainable goals. One of my teachers used to say that five minutes of sincere focused meditation is better than sitting for an hour with thoughts wandering here and there. By setting the bar low at first, you allow for success. Incremental, manageable increases will then inspire your students to strive for progress. Always be encouraging and congratulate their persistence.

---

## INSPIRE!

---

A meditation teacher and mentor is nothing if not a source of inspiration for their students. You may not think of yourself as an inspirational person, but you undoubtedly inspire others, often without knowing it. Everyone has inspired someone at one time or another. You don't need to be charismatic to inspire. Inspiration arises in moments of simple sincerity when you are just being yourself and willing to open and share yourself with others.

The more sincere you are with yourself, the more you will find yourself doing what you love to do, and the more you will inspire others to do the same. Inspiration moves like electricity from the inspired to those who want inspiration. It happens automatically and effortlessly. A fire never needs to think about how to light a fire; likewise, inspiration is not something you need to try to *do*; it is something you *are*. If meditation sincerely means something to you, others will be inspired when you share it.

So, don't be hesitant! Allow your enthusiasm to shine through. If you feel the need for validation, then find quotes from famous and inspirational figures and occasionally quote them for your students. Be sure the quotes genuinely inspire you, and don't become overly reliant on this technique. Remember, it is *you*, right there in the present moment, who are the real source of inspiration for your students.

## CHAPTER 3

# Preparing
# For Class

Where and to whom will you be teaching? This chapter applies to when you are offering a meditation class in a formal setting. If you are sharing meditation with your children at home before bed or with friends in the park, then some of these same principles will apply. Adapt this information to your specific needs.

You will not always have an ideal place to hold class. I have held classes in cramped conditions and in places with street noise and hallway commotion. I've taught in classrooms where blackboards or wall charts detracted from the ambiance I wished to create. I have taught in private homes and in impersonal public halls. I have also had the privilege of teaching in spaces dedicated solely to meditation. Every facility has an atmosphere that you must contend with. While the facility certainly matters, it is you, the teacher, who matters most. Ultimately, it is up to you to establish the right atmosphere for your class.

## PLAN AHEAD

Decide what you need for a room setup well in advance of your class, and then arrange for the facility to provide as many of your needs as possible. The less you have to bring with you and take away, the more likely your teaching experience will be pleasant. Ask yourself questions like, "Will I need a speaker's podium?" If you plan to refer to books or extensive notes, the answer is probably yes. If you like to pace about while you talk, the podium can be set to one side where it is out of your way. Do you need chairs that can be moved around in various configurations? How many will you need? (Ask for a few more than you think you will need.)

If you can visit and examine the facility in advance, do so. That way you won't be disappointed by the room and what's there or not there when you arrive. Inquire as to what else is on the venue's schedule the same time as class. Dance party? Wedding reception? Cooking class? The activities in neighboring rooms can greatly affect your class.

Wherever possible, arrange the room appropriately in advance of your audience's arrival. If you are busy setting up chairs as your students arrive, you won't be able to greet them properly, and the atmosphere of the room will not be calm and peaceful for the start of class. Your room setup should be completed early enough to allow you time to meditate and collect your thoughts before your students arrive. If a side room is available for you, you may want to use it to collect yourself while your audience gathers; however, many teachers choose to greet people as they come in. This is especially valuable for beginner classes with first time students.

## YOUR APPEARANCE

Give this one some serious thought. As a teacher, it will be better if you fulfill the audience's expectations than if you expect the audience to fulfill yours. Are you going to be teaching at a grade school? On a college campus? In a corporate setting? At a senior citizens facility? In a prison or church? Know your venue, your audience and dress accordingly. A dinner jacket with a tie won't do if your audience is wearing cutoffs and T-shirts; but the reverse is also true. A good rule of thumb is to dress *up* slightly from how you expect your audience to be dressed. It shows that you honor them and value what you are offering.

## ARRIVE EARLY

Arrive at least fifteen minutes before your audience begins to arrive. This will allow you time to address the unexpected in your class space. You may be surprised by what you find. Before you begin arranging chairs, make note of what will be behind both you and your audience. If possible, alter the arrangement so the distractions are behind your audience and not behind you. For example, at an outdoor site such as a park or public garden, there may be a sidewalk or street nearby. That means people or cars passing behind you constantly, which will be distracting for your audience. Rearrange so the sidewalk or street is behind the audience. In a public building, there may be a window looking out onto a foyer or lobby. Arrange chairs so your audience is facing away from these distractions. You may not like looking at them yourself, but it's a much better option than having your audience distracted by them.

Sometimes previewing your venue is simply not possible. You may be traveling on a tight schedule or find that your space is in use right before it becomes available to you. If possible, avoid this situation and plan for at least fifteen minutes of transition time between the previous gathering and your class. If your setup is going to be complex, allow more time. Those using the space prior to you may want to linger on after their time is up. People resent being rushed out of a room they've just used. If this happens, be diplomatic but know that if they stay on while you're trying to set up, it can create an atmosphere of tension that may linger on after your class begins. If this is the case, then one way to reestablish an environment of ease for your students may be to lengthen the first relaxation exercise before entering the deeper stages of the guided meditation.

## ATMOSPHERICS

I suggest dimming the room lights and creating a pleasant focal point at the front of the room. This gives your audience a place to focus their visual awareness. It may be a table with flowers, a candle, or perhaps a picture of an inspiring scene from nature. It may also be a wall hanging such as a mandala.

You may light incense or use an essential oil diffuser to create a pleasant aroma. This can be especially useful if the building carries food scents or other odors. Keep in mind that many people are sensitive to aromatic scents, so use them discreetly. Consider burning incense *before* the audience arrives, allowing time for the aroma to disperse and any smoke to clear. Be sure the venue allows wall hangings, candles, or such things as burning incense before using them.

## PROPS AND MATERIALS

Meditation is usually done seated with the spine as straight as is comfortable. When I teach at my yoga studio, about half the students choose to sit cross-legged on the floor, most with the support of a wall, and the other half prefer chairs. To help both groups be comfortable, it is nice to offer props they can utilize to support their posture.

At the yoga studio, we provide comfortable chairs, thin blankets that can be easily folded to support the seat or low back, and yoga blocks that can support the knees of those sitting cross-legged. Be sure to check in with the facility where you plan to hold class to ensure they have at least chairs, as most people will choose to sit in a chair.

If you plan to have students do a creative or self-expressive activity at the end of class, such as journaling or drawing, you will want to be prepared to provide and distribute the necessary materials.

## MUSIC

Soft music may be advisable, especially if there are distracting noises like outside traffic or classes in nearby rooms. Music is an excellent way to relax people when they enter a space; however, think carefully about the music you choose. Be sure it is suitable for meditation. Some commercial venues have music piped in—inquire about this when you schedule your class. If that's the case, you will want to arrange with the venue a way to silence that music in your classroom. Alternatively, you may request to utilize their audio setup for your class.

## GREETING YOUR AUDIENCE

It's a good idea to greet first-time visitors whenever possible. This sets them at ease and allows you to establish the tone you want for class. When greeting people, be warm and welcoming. Make eye contact, smile, and introduce yourself clearly. If time permits, a few words to let new visitors know what to expect can dispel any nervousness they may have.

Similarly, allow time for casual after-class conversations if they are a vital part of your teaching style, and, of course, be mindful not to create delays for those using the room after you.

## REFRESHMENTS AND SALES

If you want to serve refreshments, distribute literature, or sell books, I suggest doing it *after* class. These can become unintended distractions. Imagine how the first meditation exercise will go if some in your audience are still nibbling on snacks or thumbing through the literature you gave out. If you have a workshop or long program, consider an intermission or a couple breaks.

Before planning refreshments or book sales, check to make sure your venue allows it. If you've received free class space in a non-profit or community center, commercial sales may not be permitted. Stay safely within the regulations of the venue if you want to be invited back.

**CHAPTER 4**

# A Typical
# Meditation Class

While chapter 7 contains detailed scripts and fully fleshed out exercises, this chapter provides a basic class outline for structuring your lesson.

## THE CLASS OUTLINE

**1.** Introduce Yourself and Give Program Overview

**2.** Engage Your Audience

    **a.** Icebreaker

**3.** Discuss Meditation and Mindfulness

    **a.** Analogies

    **b.** The Science

**4.** Guide The Meditation Experience

   **a.** Energizing Exercise

   **b.** Conscious Relaxation Exercise

   **c.** Concentration Exercise

   **d.** Guided Visualization and Meditation

   **e.** Assimilation and Manifestation

**5.** Offer Next Steps

Let's take a closer look at each aspect of the class outline.

## YOUR INTRODUCTION AND PROGRAM OVERVIEW

Audiences are often most alert at the beginning of a presentation. They are curious about the speaker and eager to discover what information the speaker has to convey. Introducing yourself with poise will set the tone for class and establish a basis for your authority on the topic of meditation.

It is also helpful to give people a general sense of what will happen in the class. Let them know what topics you will be exploring and that there will be a guided meditation experience. I suggest introducing yourself in one or two sentences, then giving your audience a general idea of the program, and then introducing yourself in further detail.

For the more detailed part of your introduction, think about the things you would need to know before you could trust a stranger to teach you how to meditate. People learn best when they trust their teacher. Earn trust by being sincere and authentic. In sharing your story, choose one that relates to the practice of meditation, and stay on topic. This will demonstrate your credibility as a teacher and will let your audience know that you have a genuine interest in the subject matter and a sincere wish to share it with others.

Sharing a simple, personal anecdote—recent or far off—that portrays how meditation has helped you can go a long way in connecting you to your audience.

Here's a sample introduction I might use for myself, depending on the time available to me:

> *Hi, my name is Sujantra. I have been practicing meditation for over thirty years. I was raised Catholic and learned to meditate at a Jesuit high school where I took a class called Contemplative Prayer and Meditation. It made a great impression on me. I decided I wanted to learn to meditate for two reasons. The first was that I wanted a way to deal with the social anxiety I felt at the time; I wanted to feel calmer and more in control of my emotions in group settings. The second reason was my interest in the powers of positive thinking, psychic abilities, intuition, and the placebo effect, which is how mental belief can*

*dramatically affect a medical outcome. In college, I found a spiritual teacher from India and studied with him for twenty-seven years. During those years, I helped open a vegetarian restaurant and taught meditation around the world. Later on, I opened a yoga studio and continue to help run it today. I am very honored to be sharing meditation with you today.*

Pause here for a few minutes and create an introduction for yourself. Remember the key elements:

- ◆ Your name and relevant background information

- ◆ Why you chose to learn meditation

- ◆ How it has helped you

- ◆ What teachers or books have influenced you

- ◆ How you make use of meditation in your daily life

## ENGAGE YOUR AUDIENCE

After introducing yourself, it is time to get to know your audience so you can tailor the program to their needs. Class size and duration will determine how much time you have for this. If, for example, you are doing a thirty-minute, lunch-break meditation at a stock trading company, you might just acknowledge that work is stressful and let them know today's meditation will focus on easing that stress. Once you know the circumstances of your audience, engage their interest by highlighting one or two ways that meditation may help them specifically.

## Icebreaker

An icebreaker is a way for students to get to know each other and for you to create a warm social atmosphere. If there are over ten people in the class, you can assign them into groups of two or three and give them instructions to introduce themselves and get to know the others in their group. Specific scripting for this is in chapter 7.

If it is a smaller class, such as five to ten students, you may decide to go around the room and have each person give their name, share if they have practiced meditation before, and share what they hope to get from the class. As people say their reasons for wanting to learn meditation, you will notice the group atmosphere becoming more convivial and engaged. This social exercise will help them become more connected to the shared practice.

As mentioned earlier, most people are looking for a way to deal with stress. Fortunately, general meditation techniques can counter most forms of stress. Meditation, by its very nature, relaxes and allows the individual to gain a calmer perspective. In addressing a person's issues, always remember that your role is not that of a therapist or certified counselor (even if you are one professionally!). Your classroom role is to teach meditation and not to take on anyone's personal case history.

A good teacher will always consider the needs of his or her students. You will find that some of your students will seek healing from various forms of trauma. Some will be athletes wanting to enhance their performance. Some may work with animals and feel they need a more insightful approach. Others may be support group workers. You may receive teenagers with their various issues, and you will likely receive ordinary people seeking self-knowledge and personal enlightenment.

Through the process of getting to know each other, the students realize that they are not alone in wanting to find inner peace and happiness. Knowing that others share similar challenges will help them feel more comfortable with the journey towards inner peace. There is nothing wrong with feeling stressed and searching for answers to life's deep questions. We all deal with the same essential challenges.

## DISCUSS MEDITATION AND MINDFULNESS

If your class consists of those who are new to meditation, it will be helpful to offer at least a brief explanation of what meditation is and how it works. This will give everyone a frame of reference for the meditation experience to follow. You could use a scientific explanation drawing from information in chapter 8 of this book, or you can refer to the Sun of Awareness diagram located in chapter 6. Alternatively, you may use any of the analogies to follow in this chapter.

I like to combine a description of subjective feelings, such as inner peace and joy, with the objective findings of science, especially studies related to stress reduction. I also like to offer simple analogies to illustrate the uses and effects of meditation.

Remember that the human mind has many subtleties. You can offer relief to your students by letting them know that strict or rigid thinking is neither necessary nor advisable for effective meditation. On the contrary, personal exploration and growth require an open mind, an attitude of flexibility, and openness to change.

## Analogies

An *analogy* is a comparison of two things used for the purpose of explaining or clarifying something. When using analogies in your teaching, you will be comparing meditation to common-day phenomena.

Be sure to select easily accessible analogies. For example, it would be disorienting for your students if you used an analogy employing mechanical terminology, such as the parts of a car's engine, if they were not mechanics themselves. Instead, using an analogy involving driving a car or navigating the rules of the road may be more familiar and accessible to your audience.

Below, I've listed several analogies to get you started. You can use these examples verbatim, or you can use them as a foundation upon which to build your own.

### A Glass of Water

The meditative mind is like a glass of pure, clear water. You can see right through it. Thoughts are like sediment. When stirred up, sediment clouds the water. When we no longer see clearly, it's because our vision has been clouded by thought. Meditation stills the water and settles the sediment of thought, so the water can become pure and clear again.

## The Source of Happiness

Mundane experience seems to teach us that happiness is an external phenomenon, something that arises from the things we possess and the situations we encounter. Through meditation, we come to realize that happiness does not arise from things or from situations. It is not something others can give to us or take away from us; rather, it is something we *allow* ourselves to experience. When we allow ourselves to experience our true essence—an experience that can occur deep in meditation—we are tapping into a real source of happiness.

Let's say, for example, you are happy with a new car you purchased. Was happiness installed in the car at the factory? Is happiness radiating from the car, like a ray of light? No, what has happened is you have chosen the possession of this object to *allow* your innate happiness to come forward. The car is not the source of your happiness. Happiness comes from within you. It lies deep within. Meditation helps us access that inner depth.

## Movie Theater Analogy

Imagine you are in a dark room seated in a comfortable chair. There is a blank, dim movie screen in front of you. You know the screen is there, but you can't see it in the darkness. The room is quiet and calm, and you can sit comfortably aware of only yourself, your breathing, and the feeling of being relaxed and at ease. This is a moment of pure mind.

You then turn on the screen. At first, the screen is blank and there are no images or sounds. This is pure awareness—a soft, gentle feeling akin to the feeling of slowly becoming conscious the morning after a good night's sleep, before thoughts pour in.

A moment later, as images and sounds appear on the screen, thinking begins. The mind lights up with thoughts, as you are now viewing and immersed in the movie that is your life.

Our lives are comprised of our thoughts and feelings about ourselves, our experiences, and what others may think of us. This is what happens on the movie screen, and this is how we spend our days and most of our lives: watching and reacting to the movie of our lives.

We forget about the pure pictureless screen, upon which all the imagery appears. We forget about the pure silence before the screen is switched on.

Meditation is the journey that calms and soothes the images on the screen. Aided by our breath and our tranquil visualizations, we begin to remember the pure screen. When we slow down and calm the active imagery of the mind, we can return to pure mind. Pulling back even further, we can allow the movie to turn off. We are then able to sink into a pure awareness of being.

## The Mind is Like a Lake

In this analogy, our thoughts are the ripples on the surface of the lake. In meditation, the lake is made calm and the waves of conscious thought subside. This allows for a clearer and truer reflection to appear on the surface of the lake (the eye of the mind). We can see ourselves and our circumstances with greater clarity, and we may even see below the surface into the deep inner movements of our inmost lives.

## The Mind is Like the Sky

The still mind is like a clear blue sky, in which the sun is knowledge and happiness. The movement of thoughts through the mind is like that of clouds across the sky. Some clouds are full of light and beauty; others are dark and heavy, and they obscure the sun. Meditation is like an airplane that carries us above the clouds and into the vastness of the clear sky where we can experience clarity and the bright warmth of the sun. Meditation allows us to reconnect with our innate happiness.

## The Sun and Moon

Our inner awareness, knowledge, and light is like the sun, while our minds and thoughts are like the moon. While the sun provides the most direct and powerful light, the moonlight is just reflected sunlight. To continue the analogy, our experience of the world is through the perceptions of mind, which correlate to the indirect, reflected light of the moon. Meditation helps us turn our attention to the true source of light and knowledge, to the sun that is our deeper spirit.

**The Self as an Onion**

We are beings of many dimensions. A nice way to envision the human being is like an onion. As we peel open an onion, we see the multiple layers or sheaths that together form the onion.

The outermost layer of a person is the physical body, sometimes referred to as the sheath of food. The next layer is the nervous system and life energy, often called the sheath of prana or life force. Next is the sheath of mind, followed by the sheath of pure joy, and finally, the most subtle dimension of our being, is the soul or spirit.

Through the practice of meditation, we can discover and experience the multiple dimensions of our being. We will also find that, at different times, we are more or less conscious of the various aspects of our being.

**Your Own Analogies**

The more you ground your explanations of meditation in common everyday experience, the more your audience will understand and resonate with your insights. Choose your analogies from the topics and activities you know best.

## The Science

In Western culture, science is revered. Many audiences will find science-based explanations of meditation and mindfulness very compelling. Thankfully, the positive effects of meditation are shown in numerous scientific studies, and increasingly advanced research is being conducted to validate the power of meditation. In chapter 8, we'll explore some of this science.

## GUIDE THE MEDITATION EXPERIENCE

The meditative experience can be organized into five segments, ordered as follows: energization, conscious relaxation, concentration, guided visualization and meditation, and, finally, assimilation and manifestation. In this section we'll explore each of the five parts, but first I'll offer pointers regarding voice and verbiage, posture, and using breath to establish flow.

### Voice and Verbiage

Nothing creates an atmosphere of peace quite so convincingly as the sound of a calm voice. Think of all the things the voice tells us about a person—for instance, when the voice is high pitched or low in tone, when it is confident, relaxed, stressed, or shy and mumbling. When it is focused with intention and when it is anxious and uncertain.

The tone of your voice has as much to say as your words. In class, leverage the influence of a calm voice to project the mood and tone for your class. Your everyday speaking cadence and voice may be adequate for conveying general information to others, but a slow and careful cadence with clear pronunciation will be especially well received by your students during meditation exercises. If you are uncertain or insecure about your voice, consider recording yourself and listening back. Don't be surprised or discouraged if you don't sound exactly as you wish. Just practice and you will develop the delivery you want.

Regarding *what* you say, it's a good idea to emphasize the positive to your students. Avoid drawing the student's attention to traits or conditions that are negative. For instance, consider the phrase, "Let go of your stress and anxiety." Saying it may actually increase stress and anxiety in the student, because the mind doesn't hear the verb phrase "let go" quite as vividly as it hears the nouns "stress and anxiety."

Instead, give them a positive, concrete image to work with. For example, say, "Now imagine palm trees swaying in a tropical breeze." This imagery is peaceful and easy to access.

As you become familiar with the scripts in chapter 7, you will be able to customize them to serve your unique offering. You may choose to look up synonyms for key words in the scripts and modify the wording to suit your preferences. You may also wish to create entirely new scripts, using those offered in chapter 7 as templates.

## Posture

It is essential for the student to assume a comfortable position while meditating. However, we want both comfort *and* alertness. I do not suggest having your students do the initial exercises while lying down. The inclination to fall asleep will be too great for some to resist. Keep your students alert by keeping them upright and straight in posture. This means with as straight a spine as can be maintained in a comfortable, seated position.

## Using Breath to Establish Flow

Just as yoga is often taught by flowing transitions from one physical position to another, so too is there a "flow" to teaching a seated meditation. The flow is designed to ease the student into a calm and relaxed state. Sitting still while focusing on their breath is how class begins.

As you guide them through their breath cycles, draw upon verbal imagery to help students link their inhalation to awareness of specific parts of the body. For instance, in the Conscious Relaxation script in chapter 7, the students are instructed to release and relax the following areas as they breathe in and out: forehead, eyes, cheeks, jaw, back of the neck and shoulders, chest, solar plexus, belly, and pelvic floor. If time permits, you can become even more anatomically specific.

The inhale can correspond to becoming *aware* of the body, and the exhale can be used to *relax* the body. First, we become *aware*, then we *relax*. You'll notice your students gradually releasing tension as you guide them through this cycle of awareness and relaxation. Roughly 80% of the people to whom I have taught meditation are primarily interested in stress reduction. This initial exercise powerfully sets the stage for addressing their needs.

As you guide class, check in with yourself periodically to recognize your own breathing patterns and to nurture your own inner relaxation. Speak slowly, calmly, and clearly during the exercise. Your relaxed state will contribute to a peaceful ambiance. Reading the scripts in a calm but alert manner will add much to the effectiveness of the exercise.

## Part 1: Energizing Exercise

For your audience to reap the most benefit from the meditative experience, it is important they be alert and energized. It's possible your class attendees will have just come from work. They may be feeling lethargic or even mildly agitated. After ten or fifteen minutes of listening to your introduction and topics of discussion, they will want to energize their physical bodies prior to entering the deeper meditation.

The simplest energizing techniques can be done while seated, including shoulder shrugs, gentle neck rolls, and a few arm movements. You may also have the audience stand up and move their bodies a bit. Various yoga postures or tai chi movements can be used. If time permits and space is available, you may have people do some kind of focused walk. This should happen before the main meditation practice.

## Part 2: Conscious Relaxation

I mentioned previously that most people come to meditation classes with a hope of finding a way to manage stress. Your conscious relaxation exercise will offer them a practical way to reduce most surface-level stresses and tensions. I say "surface-level" because there may be underlying issues that require a deeper approach. The techniques offered in this book are designed to aid your students in consciously relaxing and relieving the basic tensions that accumulate in the physical body. For many, this relaxation technique of five to ten minutes will be their only meditation practice.

The conscious relaxation exercise also attempts to take the student's concentration to a deeper level. It accomplishes this by causing the student to establish a focused awareness of his or her own body. The mind is quieted by focusing on a specific sensation of the body.

## Part 3: Concentration Exercise

Now that your students have energized their bodies (Part 1) and have also consciously relaxed their bodies (Part 2), they are ready to begin to draw their concentration inward to focus on the mind's awareness of their bodily sensations. The concentration exercises given in chapter 7 focus on these bodily sensations, including the flow of the breath.

Throughout the concentration exercises, no attempt is made to silence the mind, but the student is encouraged to notice how his or her mind wanders during the exercise. By merely noticing this mental movement, the student is practicing mindfulness. When students find themselves drifting into thoughts, they learn to bring their attention back to the tactile sensation of breath. The sensation of breath is used to anchor the student's attention in the present moment.

The exercise is a two-step process:

**Step One** is for your students to become consciously aware of the mind's activity without trying to stop its activity. This is parallel to the relaxation exercise in which they became aware of their body without trying to stop any function of the body.

**Step Two** is to concentrate on a specific thought or sensation. A thought can be a positive affirmation, the visualization of a goal, or any specific idea you offer as a point of focus. If a sensation is chosen by the student, encourage them to use a pleasant one.

Sight is an excellent basis for the first concentration exercise because research has shown that about 50% of the brain is wired for sight. When offering multiple exercises based on the physical senses, I typically do a vision exercise first, followed by an auditory exercise, and then exercises that employ the senses of touch, smell, and taste.

When using hearing as the basis for a concentration exercise, you may have students focus on the *sound* of their breath rather than the tactile sensation of breath. Using *touch* as the basis, you might have them ignore the sound of their breathing and concentrate on the tactile sensations of breath, such as the rise and fall of the belly.

Continuing with sound, you may guide your students to listen carefully as they recite a word or phrase in an audible voice. This exercise is the essence of *mantra* meditation. Any voiced idea can be a mantra, even if it is voiced silently within the mind. In silent recitation, there is still a mental sensation of sound. Mantras can be a single syllable, a word, or a phrase. You can repeat a mantra in three ways: first, aloud; second, silently but with your tongue moving; and third, completely silently, with a still tongue and fully engaged mind.

Here are some examples of focused concentration, both internal and external:

### Sight
Outer example: an actual candle flame
Inner example: an imagined candle flame

### Hearing
Outer example: vocal recitation of a mantra
Inner example: silent recitation

### Touch
Outer example: real sand beneath your feet
Inner example: memory of the sensation of sand

## Smell
Outer example: the scent of a lemon
Inner example: a memory of scent

## Taste
Outer example: actual taste on the tongue
Inner example: a memory of flavor

Sometimes when guiding a class through these exercises, I leave out smell and taste and simply ask the class to be aware of their tongues. I do this by first asking them to feel the tip of their tongue as it touches the roof of their mouth. I then counteract that by having them allow the tongue to rest motionless at the bottom of the mouth. Just as stillness of the eye reduces thoughts, stillness of the tongue reduces tactile awareness of the tongue.

## Part 4.1: Guided Visualizations

Now that you have your audience relaxed in body and focused in mind, you are ready to guide them through a visualization exercise. When used during a state of concentrated awareness, visualization techniques have profound effects. Your students can be guided to apply their focused awareness toward attaining deeper insights, peace, and potential solutions to personal concerns.

In its simplest form, guiding a visualization exercise is like reading a story to a child. The best visualizations are interactive. They allow the student to make personal choices and be involved in the exercise. Giving your students the freedom to choose colors, scenes in nature, and other aspects may seem like a trivial nicety, but the effect is to personalize the exercise. It allows the students to own the experience and infuse it with what is meaningful and relevant to them.

In visualization exercises, you will guide students to imagine, in their mind's eye, the realities they wish to create in their lives. It will help to include as many of the physical senses as is practical. You may describe settings, such as a tranquil seaside, to help them connect to feelings and emotions. You may also guide them to a place where they can visualize different options or solutions available to them regarding choices they must make or challenges they face.

To understand the power of visualization, look at the room around you. Everything you see began with someone's idea. By acting on ideas, things were created. Everything begins with thought; visualizations are simply focused thoughts.

Visualization techniques serve a great many subsets of students. Take, for example, someone who seeks a new career. They can now better evaluate their options in a calm state of mind and more objectively assess their personal strengths and weakness. This corresponds to *outer* clarity. They may also discover a clearer sense of where their heart is genuinely drawn. This would be *inner* clarity.

If you are working with a group focused on intention setting, goal setting, or performance, visualizations are especially useful. Some may wish to lift their standard of living in a financial way, become more compassionate in their interactions with others, or simply feel more gratitude and satisfaction with what they have. If you find yourself teaching athletes, you could have them visualize themselves going through the motions of their activity or seeing and feeling themselves remaining calm during competition. People looking to heal will benefit from a heart-centered visualization.

Our lives can be shaped by our ability to foster internal and external awareness, to focus that awareness, and to concentrate our energies on visualized goals. These tools of self-empowerment are sharpened through the regular practice of meditation.

## Part 4.2: Meditation

Meditation flows naturally from concentration and visualization techniques. One way to think of it is like the movement of a horse. That movement, broken down into progressive phases, is walking, trotting, cantering, and galloping. One flows into the next. It is the same with concentration, visualization, and meditation.

Meditation is the deepest element of practice. Chapter 7 offers guidance on how long to keep your students in meditation, how often you speak, and what you can say.

With regular practice, a person's meditation can advance to the point where he or she feels a greater force at work in his or her life than just that of personal effort. The person's effort is now augmented by this greater force. Many come to feel their very hearts sustained by this greater force, which not only gives comfort in times of disappointment or failure but also gives rise to a personal faith that carries the meditator through personal endeavors of all sorts. How? By allowing them to see and feel the greater force within, the person they really are.

At this advanced stage, the meditator passes into a practice of surrendering him or herself to the practice itself, which contains infinite revelations of peace, love, and wisdom.

At the end of the meditation, always allow two to three minutes for students to exit their personal experiences. Give them advance notice that the meditation will end in two minutes and suggest they begin concluding whichever technique they are engaged in. After this transition period, slowly guide their awareness toward the external surroundings while suggesting they keep some of their awareness focused on the inner feelings or inspiration they received from their meditation.

## Part 5: Assimilation and Manifestation

The conclusion of the formal meditation is not the end of the experience. Feeling peace within or finding the inspiration to envision life in a new way can naturally flow into outer activity. As much as possible we want to help students assimilate and then manifest in their day-to-day lives the experiences they have in meditation.

If time permits, suggest they take a few minutes to write down any thoughts or feelings they experienced during the meditation, especially positive ones they wish to reflect upon later. Occasional reflection is an effective way to keep aspirations alive and inspiration fresh. Some may prefer to draw, write a poem, or play an instrument, and these are great options, too. Any form of tangible self-expression is a wonderful way to assimilate their meditation experience.

The next step is manifestation. Just as a beautiful tree begins with a small seed, so too our lives blossom from the seeds of our inmost thoughts and inspirations. During meditation, we cultivate visionary seeds for the future; we unearth revelations of what we wish to create in our lives. Taking steps toward realizing our visions is what I call manifesting our meditation. A regular practice will soon be seen as the catalyst that speeds the materialization of our desires.

## ENDING CLASS AND NEXT STEPS

The final segment of your class is to offer students a path forward in their practice. The students have hopefully gained a genuine experience of meditation through your offering. It may end up being the only meditative experience they have in their entire lives, or it may be the first in a series of a lifelong practice. That is up to them. You've done your part by guiding them through the experience.

Studies suggest that the average person carries away about three key points from any presentation; so, be sure to reiterate a few impactful takeaways from your class. End by offering them encouragement to keep up the practice, suggesting applicable resources such as books, apps, or websites, and thanking them for being there. Mention the classes you offer, and invite them back!

## CHAPTER 5

# Teaching Meditation
# to Children

Meditation can be just as life-altering for children and teenagers as it is for adults. Thankfully, teaching meditation to children can be approached in much the same way as teaching to adults.

I learned to meditate when I was in the eleventh grade. It helped me deal with social and personal challenges I faced at the time. I learned to focus on my breathing, relax my body, and observe my thoughts and patterns of thought with a healthy sense of detachment. For example, I came to realize that worrying about whether or not someone liked me may not be a worthwhile spend of mental and emotional energy.

Visualizations for children can be thought of as storytelling infused with deep insights and a focus on developing inner awareness. Meditation gives children an experience of tangible inner peace that can serve as a barometer by which they gauge other life experiences. It can be a valuable reference point for when they need to evaluate situations and make decisions.

Children experience stress of many kinds. You can help children deal with stress by showing them how to notice the signs of stress and by offering healthy coping practices for them to use when navigating difficult situations. Offering them the peaceful experience of mindfulness lets them know there are alternatives to worry and fear.

Furthermore, the meditation experience nurtures lifelong skillsets used in learning, socializing, cultivating healthy relationships, and developing a solid sense of self.

## CHILDHOOD STRESS

Childhood stress can be present in any setting that requires children to adapt or change. Stress may be caused by positive changes such as starting a new activity, but most commonly it is linked with difficult transitions such as pubescence, social dynamics, illness, or disturbances in family life. In small amounts, stress can be good, but excessive stress can detrimentally affect the way a child thinks, acts, and feels.

Because children need time to learn how to respond to stress as they grow and develop, stressful events that are easily managed by an adult may be challenging for a child. Even small changes can impact a child's sense of safety and security.

Stressors for children include:

♦ Worrying about schoolwork or grades

♦ Juggling responsibilities: school, chores, sports

♦ Problems with friends, bullying, and peer-group pressures

♦ Moving, changing schools, dealing with living arrangements or homelessness

♦ Having negative thoughts about themselves, or low self-esteem

♦ Going through physical changes

♦ Witnessing parental divorce or separation

♦ Money problems in the family

♦ Living in an unsafe home or neighborhood

♦ Influences from the media and hearing adults talk about the news

In addition to the list above, some children are stressed because their time is overscheduled by well-meaning adults. Research has shown that some children are too busy to have time to play creatively or relax after school. Their parasympathetic nervous systems (the rest-and-digest system) have not been given the time or appropriate conditions to help them reset. Children who complain about their activities or express disinterest in participating in them may be overscheduled. Talk to your children about how they feel about their extracurricular activities. If they complain, discuss the pros and cons of stopping one activity. If stopping isn't an option, explore ways to help manage a child's time and responsibilities to lessen the anxiety.

## HOW TO CHOOSE MEDITATION TECHNIQUES FOR CHILDREN

The meditation techniques you choose for children will depend on their level of cognitive development. In my teaching, I have drawn from the research of Swiss psychologist Jean Piaget (1896-1980), a pioneer in mapping the stages of cognitive development in children. His work was groundbreaking and continues to be the basis of other foundational studies.

To effectively engage children in meditation, you need to know their present level of development and meet them at that level. Knowing the *next* stage in their development will help you select techniques that will stimulate their growth.

When I was ten or eleven, an aunt of mine began to ask me questions like, "If a tree falls in the forest and no one is present to hear it fall, does it make a sound?" She also asked me, "Did you exist before you were born?" and "How does a huge tree emerge from a small seed?"

Questions like these, presented amid safe and relaxed conditions, prompted me to ponder and use my mind in new ways.

It is beyond the scope of this book to explore in detail the developmental stages of childhood, so I encourage you to do additional study. That said, the brief overview below, combined with your own careful observations of the children you work with and the range of other techniques offered in this book, should enable you to successfully offer meditation to children.

## STAGES OF DEVELOPMENT

The Preoperational Stage of Development begins around age two and continues through age seven. This stage is characterized by the development of symbolic thought. Techniques for this stage include linking movement to breath, linking movement to imaginative visualization, and linking movement with symbolic play. At this stage, the child's mind is likely to believe everything it takes in. The child lives in the realm of sensation. Accordingly, you will want to help children awaken their senses, imagination, and curiosity about the world.

The Concrete Operational Stage of Development is typically from ages seven to twelve. As the name implies, this stage is characterized by the development of operational thought. Meditation techniques useful during this stage include those for children in the Preoperational Stage, but the visualizations can be longer in duration, more detailed, and filled with deeper meaning. Time, space, cause, and effect take on deeper significance.

The Formal Operational Stage of Development begins in adolescence and continues through adulthood. It is characterized by abstract thinking and the understanding that different choices lead to different outcomes. Metacognition is now possible, meaning children can observe their own thinking and consciously control their own thoughts.

In addition to Piaget's work, two of my favorite resources are the *Hand Model of the Brain* and *Upstairs Downstairs Brain* by Dr. Daniel Siegel. Performing a web search of these terms will yield infographics, videos, and other materials for using and teaching these models. Essentially, they offer children a way to visualize their bodies, thoughts, and emotions in a way that helps them recognize, understand, and regulate themselves.

## INTEGRATING MEDITATION INTO SCHOLASTIC ACTIVITIES

*The value of education is not the learning of many facts but the training of the mind to think.*

—ALBERT EINSTEIN

Many teachers express concern that strict academic guidelines and schedules may not allow space for meditation and conscious relaxation in the classroom. Luckily, children can learn to use their mental capacity in new and exciting ways while staying within curriculum bounds.

The techniques can boost concentration, brighten the imagination, heighten abstract thinking, expand empathetic awareness, and create a greater capacity for self-reflection and insight—all cognitive skills which can improve scholastic performance.

## Science

♦ When studying the principles of nature, have students visualize a principle in action, and then have them imagine that same force operating in their own minds and bodies. For example, the constant cycle of day and night: sometimes we are full of energy (daytime), and other times we grow quiet and need reflection (evening). Nature is in a constant state of change, and so are our bodies and minds. These changes are natural and healthy.

♦ Einstein used thought experiments to derive basic principles in his Theory of Relativity. Allow children time to use their imaginations to visualize a comet's orbit or the movement of an asteroid belt. Prompt them to feel the pull of gravity on their bodies.

♦ When teaching about the parasympathetic nervous system (rest and digest), include some science-based figures that back the meditation experience.

## Math

♦ Encourage students to visualize numbers or see multiplication in their minds. They can also imagine numbers as animals or objects. One is a candle, two is a swan, and so on. Allow numbers to become an enjoyable part of thinking and not something to be feared.

♦ Link geometry to cubist paintings, or link division to the frets on a guitar. Explore how dividing a guitar string in half changes the pitch. Hum along with the various notes.


## Language Arts

♦ Encourage closed eyes and imaginative listening to well-written literature. Encourage visualizations that allow the children to feel the scenes and characters.

♦ Explore listening with feeling to rhythmic, rhymed poetry. *Prosody*, a term referring to the patterns of rhythm and sound in language, is known to prompt relaxation in the nervous system.

♦ Play with letters in the mind. Play with anagrams in the mind's eye, for example: listen = silent.


## History

♦ Offer and allow visualization in class. For example, encourage empathy towards people of the past. What might the students have done if confronted with x, y, z situation in history?

# CONCLUSION

Giving children a way to understand their bodies, thoughts, moods, and emotions will be invaluable to their personal growth. Meditation may show them how much agency they have over these aspects of themselves. The course of my own life was altered positively by the childhood experience of meditation.

As a teacher of meditation, you have the potential to profoundly influence the development of growing children. By giving them the experience of inner peace, you offer them a reference point for all that may come their way. You can guide children to find peace through meditation simply by adapting the techniques in this book to their level of cognitive development.

## CHAPTER 6

# The Sun of
# Awareness

## EXPLANATION FOR THE SUN OF AWARENESS

As we mature, we begin to think abstractly. Mathematics, philosophy, ethics, psychology, empathy, and a range of other subjects depend upon and help to deepen abstract thinking. Many of us will also develop the ability to ponder our own thoughts and mental habits, a process called *metacognition.* Students can explore their cognition within the framework of The Sun of Awareness diagram. This awareness will be invaluable as they journey through life.

In the diagram, the center of the Sun represents the subjective awareness of Self: one's fundamental feeling of being. It can be equated with the thought "I am." As children, we develop this state unconsciously. Through meditative practices and spiritual quests, we seek to reconnect with this dimension of ourselves consciously. This is the realm of the mystical and transcendental.

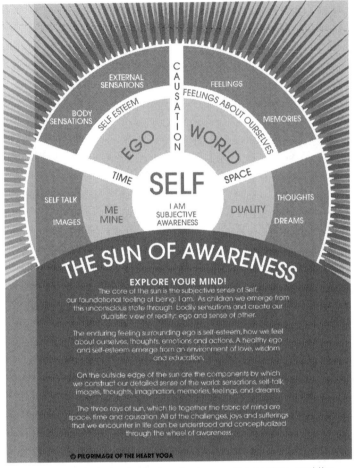

*A diagram to help students reflect upon themselves and the nature of being.*

As young children become conscious of bodily sensations and external environments, they develop an awareness of the world and a sense of themselves in the world. At this point, the ego and a dualistic sense of oneself in the world emerge from the Self. In other words, the child begins to see herself, her ego, as separate from the world she lives in. The enduring feeling surrounding ego is self-esteem: how we feel about ourselves, our thoughts, emotions, and actions. A healthy ego and positive sense of self-esteem emerge from environments of love, wisdom, and learning.

On the outer edge of the Sun are the components we use to construct our sense of the world: a composite of bodily sensations, external sensations, self-talk, thoughts, memories, feelings, and dreams.

The rays of the Sun that tie together the fabric of mind are the concepts of space, time, and causation (cause and effect.)

A healthy person is aware of all parts of the wheel and aims to keep them in balance. She has a holistic view of herself. She regards herself with love, compassion, understanding, and good humor. She possesses a healthy ego and positive self-esteem. She acknowledges valuable thoughts and memories and discards unnecessary worries and anxieties.

Furthermore, the well-balanced individual holds personalized worldviews while acknowledging that the views of others, even if different from one's own, are also valid. Imbalance occurs when we do not think well of ourselves, we fixate on unhelpful thoughts or feelings, and we think our ideas and perceptions are the only valid perspective.

The meditation techniques in this book are designed to help both children and adults explore themselves and discover a wider range of cognitive abilities. All the challenges, joys, and natural experiences we encounter in life can be conceptualized through the Sun of Awareness.

# CHAPTER 7

# Class Scripts

This chapter contains sample scripts that can serve as a foundation for you as you teach. The approximate amount of time required to complete each exercise is listed under each title. The actual duration will depend on your cadence and the class format you choose. Feel free to adapt the scripts to your teaching situation and preferences.

Each script begins with a quotation-mark graphic to help you visually keep your place in the text if you intend to read directly from the book during class. **Teacher Notes** are bolded and italicized throughout the text; these are intended to offer you guidance, not to be read aloud in class. As discussed in chapter 1, most students will have their eyes closed throughout the meditation, so don't worry if you need to read from the text. With experience, you will develop your own scripts and style of presentation.

Remember, too, to pause from time to time. Students appreciate the time to experience what you are guiding them through. I have found the best way to regulate the pace of my class is by counting my breath cycles (one or two complete inhales and exhales) during the pauses. My relaxed breath cycle is about seven to ten seconds. Pause length suggestions, measured in breath cycles, are included in many of the scripts below.

## ORCHESTRATING AN ICEBREAKER

*Ten minutes*

A classroom setting can feel tense and formal if the group is not given an opportunity to express themselves and connect with each other. An icebreaker is used to relieve this tension.

I like to break up the group into smaller groups of three. I determine the groups by either pointing out who will be in what group, or I have people count, one by one, up to a predetermined value and then group according to the number they called out. For instance, if there are twenty-seven people in the class, I would have people count to nine a total of three times and then have those who called the same number gather together.

Once the students are in their respective groups, I let them know this will be a ten-minute exercise. I instruct them to share their names, why they want to learn meditation, and what their favorite food or restaurant is. I also give advance notice that when we return to the larger group, each person from the small group will introduce one other person from their group by giving their name, reason for meditating and favorite food. Although some people may be long-winded in the smaller groups, the larger group introductions usually go quickly. Depending on time constraints, I may not do this round-robin introduction.

Alternative questions the small group could explore:

♦ Favorite book or movie

♦ Where they were born

♦ Favorite pastime or hobby

## PART 1: ENERGIZING EXERCISE

*Two to four minutes*

**Teacher Note:** *The meditative experience is launched by waking up the physical body. Lethargy, both mental and physical, impede the ability to meditate. Energizing exercises enliven the physical body, boost the students' awareness of their energetic bodies (nervous system and mind), and help them begin to release the tensions or mental chatter they may have brought in with them.*

Begin by sitting upright, keeping your spine as straight as is comfortable. Feel your spine lifting and becoming energized. Place your hands palms down on your thighs.

As you breathe in, move your shoulders forward and up. As you breathe out, release your shoulders back and down.

Imagine a thread connected to the top of your head. As you inhale, your head and spine will lift and lengthen as if gently tugged by the thread. As you exhale, maintain that length while allowing your muscles to relax.

Keeping a straight spine, draw attention to your neck muscles by turning your head to the right, then back to center, to the left, then back to center.

Take a slow breath in. As you do, feel your neck lengthening. On the exhale, allow your chin to drop to your chest and feel how this releases the muscles at the back of the neck.

On the next inhale, lift your head back to a neutral position. Exhale and let your head drop backward, allowing your throat to open and your jaw to release. If comfortable, hold this position for another round of breath, then gently lift your head back to the neutral position.

On your next in breath, make a lion's face by opening your eyes and mouth as wide as you can. As you
exhale, counteract this open face by squeezing your
eyes shut, pursing your lips, and scrunching your fa-
cial muscles. Repeat this three times.

## PART 2: CONSCIOUS RELAXATION EXERCISES

**Teacher Note:** *The following exercises help students set-
tle in, relax, and enter a frame of mind where they can
consciously release stress. I suggest always including a
Preliminary Breathing Exercise. Class duration and your
personal preference can then dictate whether you follow
up the breathing exercise with the Conscious Relaxation
script, the Body Scan Exercise, or both.*

### A Preliminary Breathing Exercise

*Two minutes*

We'll now connect and tune into our breath. One of
the great secrets of meditation is that the breath and
the mind are intertwined. As you deepen and slow
your breath, you slow your brain waves, and by slowing

your brain waves, you gain access to your autonomic nervous system, a system that functions largely unconsciously. Just by slowing the breath, you can tap into these deeper brain states and consciously prompt your own relaxation, calm, and focus.

Breathe in and out as slowly as is comfortable. Focus on the sensation of your breath. Feel your body breathing. Notice how you have control over the process of becoming more and more relaxed.

## Conscious Relaxation

*Five to ten minutes*

**Teacher Note:** *Allow time for two to three breath cycles between each paragraph.*

Let's start by finding a comfortable position. Hold a posture that is as straight as is comfortable. This will help you stay alert during the practice. You may close your eyes during this exercise, but if you become drowsy, then consider opening your eyes enough to keep you alert. To experience meditation, you must pass through the realm where most people fall asleep. This involves moving your body into a state of deep relaxation while remaining awake and present.

As you breathe in, become aware of the muscles in your forehead; as you exhale, allow those muscles to relax.

As you breathe in, become aware of the muscles around your eyes; as you exhale, allow those muscles to soften.

As you breathe in, become aware of the muscles in your cheeks; as you exhale, allow those muscles to melt.

As you breathe in, become aware of the muscles in your jaw; as you exhale, allow those muscles to unwind.

As you breathe in, become aware of the muscles in the back of your neck and shoulders; as you breathe out, loosen those muscles, and allow them to fall at ease.

As you breathe in, become aware of the muscles in your chest; as you exhale, allow those muscles to release.

As you breathe in, become aware of the muscles in your solar plexus; as you exhale, allow those muscles to let go.

As you breathe in, become aware of the muscles in your belly; as you exhale, allow those muscles to be fully at ease.

As you breathe in, send your awareness to the base of your torso, your pelvic floor; as you exhale, allow those muscles to rest.

As you breathe in, become aware of the many muscles of your body; as you exhale, allow your whole body to soften completely.

To bring yourself out of this relaxed internal awareness, begin to wiggle your fingers and toes. Allow your breath to return to its natural rhythm. Slowly open your eyes and become aware of your environment. As you make this transition, notice the relaxation you've cultivated within yourself.

## The Body Scan Exercise

*Ten to fifteen minutes but may vary*

**Teacher Note:** *The aim of the Body Scan Exercise is to observe bodily sensations while remaining relatively motionless. Without changing physical positions, students focus on the sensations present throughout the body, including neutral sensations that may normally escape their attention. Encourage students to observe any and all sensations that may pass through their bodies during this exercise, not just those normally noticed.*

*Have your students assume a comfortable position. This could be sitting upright, but for students who are* comfortable doing so, lying on their backs is particularly beneficial. They may support their bodies with a prop or two, such as a folded blanket to support the head and neck or a rolled blanket for under the backs of the knees.

Start with the feet and move upwards to the head. At the end of the body scan, instruct students to slowly come back to their external senses through gentle movements.

Allow time for three breath cycles between each paragraph.

"

Gently close the eyes or soften the gaze and bring awareness into the body. Start to focus your awareness on any physical sensations in or on your body. Simply notice what you feel. Notice the sensation of breathing and allow the cadence of your breath to happen naturally and automatically, without trying to breathe in any particular way. Observe the places in the body where you feel the sensations of breath. Perhaps this is at the tip of the nostrils or in the belly.

Take a moment to notice the activity of the mind: lingering thoughts, mental chatter, or memories. There is no need to try to stop these thoughts—simply become aware that the thoughts are there. Then, redirect your attention back to the sensations of the body.

Next, notice if emotions are present. There may be strong feelings or not much emotion at all. Either way, acknowledge your current emotional state without trying to change it. Allow emotions to be part of your awareness, then return your attention to the sensations of breath.

Now, direct your attention to your feet. Notice any sensations present in the feet: the toes, the tops of the feet, the soles, the heels, and the ankles. Attune to the present sensations, noticing what you can without needing to move or adjust positions.

Now, move the attention to the lower legs. Observe any sensations present in the shins and calves. Notice the knee joints: the fronts of the knees, backs of the knees, and sides of the knees.

Now, move the attention to the upper legs. What sensations are present in the fronts and backs of the thighs?

Now, draw your attention to the hip area: the front of the pelvis, the sacral area, the buttocks, and the pelvic floor. Observe the sensations here.

Now, move the attention to the torso. Begin by noticing the sensations in the back of your torso. Then, bring your awareness around to the front of the torso.

What feelings are present in the belly, the rib cage, the area around the heart, and the collarbones? Be present with these sensations.

Now, transport your attention down into the arms and hands. Notice your fingers, the palms of your hands, the backs of your hands, and your wrists. Observe your forearms, elbows, upper arms, and shoulders. What do you feel in these areas?

Now, move your attention up into the neck. Notice any sensations in the throat area and in the back of the neck. Pause and acknowledge these sensations, and then continue up into the head. Observe the mouth: the jaw, the lips, the tongue, and teeth. Remember, no need to change anything; just acknowledge the sensations that are present.

Observe the cheeks and nose, the muscles around the eyes, the eyelids, the eyes themselves, and all the muscles of the forehead and temples. Observe the sensations in the scalp, both at the top of the head and the back of the head. Mentally observe your ears. Take time here to be present with the sensations in the neck and head.

Now, release your focused awareness from the parts of the body and bring the attention back to the breath. Notice the feelings brought about by inhaling and exhaling. Imagine and visualize your breath journeying through the whole body. Feel how the traveling breath connects all parts of the body.

As we move toward the end of this body scan exercise, take a moment to thank yourself for showing up for yourself, for being present with your body, and for cultivating your wellbeing without needing to change anything.

## PART 3: CONCENTRATION EXERCISES

*Five to ten minutes*

**Teacher Note:** *Now that students are relaxed, alert, and aware, it's a good time to practice focusing their awareness and sharpening their concentration. For the concentration exercises, you may want to light a candle, place flowers in the front of the room, or turn on music for the students to focus on. Music, if played, should be relaxing and instrumental. Typing "meditation music" into any of the streaming services will result in a great selection to choose from.*

## Concentration on the External Senses

**Teacher Note:** *Allow time for three to five breath cycles between each paragraph.*

"

Open your eyes enough to concentrate on one object in your field of awareness. Let your eyes rest on the object. It's okay to blink, and it's okay if your vision blurs. Just allow your eyes to remain on that single object.

Now, close your eyes and place your focus on external sounds. Your mind may want to label the sounds, but feel free to release this instinct to label and instead lean into the texture, duration, and pitch of the sounds.

Now, focus in on one sound and let the other sounds fall away. Commit your attention to the one sound you choose.

Now, shift your awareness to your breath. Feel your breath passing in and out of your nostrils. Follow your breath in and out of your lungs. Bring your awareness to your chest and feel the beating of your heart. With each exhalation, feel your heart and chest relaxing.

## Concentration on the Heartbeat and Pulses in the Body

"

On your next inhalation, hold your breath for a few seconds and try to locate the beat of your heart. Your heart is nestled between your lungs and slightly to the left side of your chest. Continue breathing. As you try to trace your heartbeat, gently bring your thumb to your pointer finger and feel the pulse in the pads of your fingers. Once you feel the pulse, you may move your awareness to different parts of your body and feel the myriad pulsations of energy in your body. Maybe you feel the pulse in your wrists, your armpits, or your arms. Enjoy the sensations of life energy pulsing through your body.

**Teacher Note:** *Allow time here for ten to twenty breath cycles.*

## Concentration on the Internal Senses

"

Allow your eyelids to gently close, and become aware of your eyeballs. Imagine you are standing near the seaside. Feel your eyes move as you look out at the ocean; look up into the sky; look at people walking past, at seagulls flying by, or any other objects of awareness upon which you wish to rest your gaze.

Now, bring your eyes to a point of stillness and look straight ahead.

Now we'll gently warm up the muscles around the eyes. Keeping the eyelids closed, look upward and pause. Then, slowly track your inner gaze downward. Next, look over to the left, over to the right, and back to center.

Now lift your gaze slightly upward toward the center of your forehead, a finger's width above your brow line.

Keeping your eyes still, bring your awareness to your tongue. Touch the tip of your tongue to the roof of your mouth, aware of that point of contact.

Now, allow your tongue to sink to the bottom of your mouth and rest motionless.

Next, bring your awareness to the back of your throat and create a slight contraction with the glottis. This is the same contraction you would do if you were going to fog a mirror. While holding this contraction and breathing through your nose, you may notice your breath become audible, especially on the exhalation. Enjoy this textured breathing for a few rounds of breath.

For the next five to ten breaths, feel free to rest your attention on the technique you most preferred.

## Concentration on Breath Awareness

*Five to ten minutes*

**Teacher Note:** *This concentration exercise anchors the student's attention in the present moment by focusing on the bodily sensations of breath. As the exercise continues, you may remind students that it is normal for the mind to wander and that by noticing the comings and goings of thoughts, they are practicing mindfulness. Once aware their minds are wandering, they can simply direct their attention back to the breath.*

*Allow time for five to ten breath cycles between each paragraph.*

Begin by sitting in a comfortable and upright position. If you are seated on the floor, consider placing folded blankets under your bottom. Feel free to lean against a wall. If you are seated on a chair, place the soles of your feet flat on the floor or on blocks, if necessary. Allow your hands to rest lightly in your lap. Sit tall with the crown of your head lifted toward the ceiling.

Gently close your eyes and place your attention on your breath. Don't change anything; just observe the natural flow of your breath as it travels in and out. It doesn't matter if your breath is long, short, deep, or shallow. Simply be aware of each breath as it happens in the present moment.

Place your attention on the most pronounced sensations of your breath—perhaps the rise and fall of the belly or the flow of air at the tips of the nostrils. Focus on the aspect of your breath that seems most noticeable to you.

If you discover your mind wandering, realize that this is the way the mind naturally functions. Simply notice it happening and that it distracts you from focusing on your breath. Then, gently bring your attention back to your breath and, once again, follow the sensations of inhaling and exhaling. Use your breath awareness to ground you in the present moment. Allow each breath to calm the body and refresh the attention.

# PART 4: GUIDED VISUALIZATIONS AND MEDITATIONS

Guided visualizations and meditation techniques flow well into each other. While visualizations can be used on their own for problem solving and decision making, they can also lead to meditation. A guided visualization directs students to use the power of their minds and imaginations to move themselves into different states of awareness. Reading a story to a child can be considered a form of guided visualization.

As you guide visualizations, give your students the opportunity to make choices. Get them involved in the process. For example, allow them to choose the quality they want to enhance in their life. Let them choose colors, scenes from nature, and other aspects of their inner landscape. When creating guided visualizations, include as many of the senses as possible. Be sure to use sight, sound, and touch, with taste and smell being optional, so that the experience is immersive and impactful.

Visualization scripting is based on the principle of three verifiable statements followed by one guiding statement. The *verifiable* statements help establish what the student's sensual experience would realistically be in the place you are guiding them toward. These statements involve descriptions of physical sensations which vivify the experience. The *guiding* statement sets out where you intend the exercise to lead them—this is usually an inner state of being.

Let's say you have asked the students to focus on a quality they would like to cultivate, or perhaps you have suggested a quality such as peace. The 3/1 formula would look like this:

Intro: Today we will visualize an ocean setting. It can be an ocean scene from your imagination, or it can be an ocean scene you recall from real life, a picture, or a painting. Imagine you are standing near the shore of a serene, sweeping ocean.

Three verifiable statements:

♦ You look out and see the vast ocean and the rich colors in the sky

♦ You feel the sand between your toes and the warmth of the sun on your skin

♦ You hear the waves lapping along the shore

One leading statement:

♦ As you breathe in, you're filled with peace and calm; as you exhale, your body relaxes

This 3/1 formula is the basic format to follow, though you may create prolonged, descriptive sections, for example a lengthier journey through a forest to a magical cabin. In the following scripts, feel free to lengthen or shorten the visualization journey depending on your needs.

## Visualization Scripts

*Hold each image for three rounds of breath.*

**Ocean**

"

In this visualization, we will focus on peace. Imagine yourself at the ocean. Either remember a place you have been or use your imagination to picture a serene ocean setting. Imagine you are standing on the shore of the ocean.

You look out and see the vast ocean and the mix of colors in the sky. You feel the sand beneath your feet and the sun's warmth upon your skin. You hear the gentle lapping of the waves. As you breathe in, you fill up with peace and calm. As you exhale, your body relaxes.

Walk down to the water's edge. Feel the soft spray of the ocean. Hear the water rolling in and out along the shoreline. Notice the ample space across the blue water. Feel inside yourself the energy of creation pulsing with the sea.

You look up and see a bird in flight. Children play nearby, and you hear their laughter. You feel a soft breeze brush your body and the vitality of the sea and nature all around you.

Now imagine the day has passed and the orange sun is setting low in the sky. The ocean is smooth and calm, and there is quietness all around you. As you breathe in and out, recognize that you are a part of the peace of the evening.

**Forest**

Imagine you are in a lush forest in the late afternoon. You are walking along a path among tall, ancient trees. Sunlight shines through the canopy, and you sense the moist forest air. As you observe the quietude of the forest, you feel that same stillness within yourself.

You notice the deep green plants and the strong limbs of the trees. You hear the occasional chirping of birds, and you take in the rich scent of earth. The forest is alive with ancient energy, and you feel that same life force moving through your veins.

You come to a clearing with a beautiful meadow. The sky stretches in every direction above the meadow. The grasses sway lazily in the breeze. Across the meadow, you see a small cottage. You know that inside the cottage a wise person lives. The cottage dweller has insight to offer you.

You walk across the meadow and feel the tender earth beneath your feet. The warm afternoon air caresses your skin. The sun illumines your way. You come to the wooden door of the cottage. You feel warmth in your heart as the wise cottage dweller opens the door to greet you.

## Heart Center Meditation

*Three to five minutes*

As you breathe in, feel your lungs filling and chest expanding. As you exhale, feel release in your chest. Continue this rhythm of expansion and release for three cycles of breath.

Now, as you breathe in, imagine you are filling your chest with life-affirming energy. Select a color for that energy. As you exhale, release and relax.

As you breathe in, feel that energy filling your heart, bringing optimism and hope. As you exhale, release the energy into your surroundings.

As you breathe in, imagine the energy is a beautiful melody that carries a warm and caring feeling that washes over you. As you exhale, feel this energy ex-ude from you.

# Tune and Brighten the Mind

*Five to ten minutes*

In this exercise, we're going to become aware of our bodily senses, one after the other.

First, become aware of the tranquility within your body. If some parts of the body do not feel tranquil at the moment, then try to release muscle groups in that area on the exhale. Place special awareness on the parts that do feel calm.

Using this awareness of the natural harmony within our bodies, we can begin to tune our minds through our senses.

**Sight**
Become aware of your eyes. With eyelids closed, become aware of your eyeballs beneath your eyelids. Move your eyes up, down, left, right, and back to center.

**Sound**
Slowly send your awareness to your ears. Focus on your ears, but not on hearing.

**Touch**
Slowly shift your awareness to your hands—just your hands themselves, not any sensation of feeling in them.

**Taste**

Slowly direct your awareness to your tongue. Move your tongue slightly, just as you did your eyes. Now, let your tongue fall motionless, and simply be aware of it.

**Smell**

Slowly draw your awareness to your nose. The cell receptors for your sense of smell are far up your nasal passageway. Perhaps you can guide your awareness up your nasal passage to those cell receptors.

**Teacher Note:** *You may want to take them on this journey through their senses one more time.*

## Shift to Focus on Sensation

We've been focusing on the organs of sensation. Now we will focus on sensation itself.

Bring awareness to your eyes again. With eyes closed, gaze into the backs of your eyelids and notice any light patterns or displays. Maybe you see shifting patterns, little sparkles of light, or other shapes dancing on the backs of your eyelids. Maybe you see a simple black screen. Whatever it is you see, focus on the sensation of seeing.

Now, draw your awareness to your ears and focus in on the sounds you hear.

Now, shift your awareness to your tongue. What taste sensations are on or around it?

Next, bring your awareness to your nose. Which scents do you detect?

To experience the sensation of touch, connect the palm of your hand to the pointer finger of the other hand. Move your finger back and forth, focusing on the sensations of touch.

As you breathe in and out, notice the sensations involved in being alive in this moment. Allow yourself to feel any or all present sensations, be they sight, sound, touch, taste, or scent. Maybe you notice your clothing, your feet upon the floor, or your body resting in the chair. Enjoy the sensations in their pure form.

While experiencing these sensations, your mind may affix labels to them. Let that happen, but then tune back into the sensation itself as much as possible.

> Amidst all this sensation, become aware of yourself as the observer. After all, it's you who observes these sights, sounds, and sensations.
>
> Allow yourself to relax into this calm and centered feeling.

### The Observer and the Observed

*Seven to fifteen minutes*

**Teacher Note:** *In this exercise, you may interchange the term "the observer" with "the witness" and "the enjoyer." People will likely resonate with one or the other of these terms. For example, I find the word "witness" to evoke a feeling of detachment, which is different from the feeling I get from "enjoyer." Each works well but brings about a different effect, which is why you may interchange them as you guide your students.*

*The Observer exercise requires steady focus. It is divided into six areas of awareness: the world around us, the subtle elements, the organs of action, the organs of perception, the subtle realms of mind, and the experience of "I am." It is a powerful technique that can take students into a deep awareness but may also be too advanced for some. Try it yourself, then determine which aspects are best for your offering. For example, you may choose to do only the first two areas of awareness or do the first two and then jump to the fifth and sixth. Again, experiment on your own first with these techniques.*

*Allow time for three breath cycles between each paragraph.*

"

In this exercise, we identify and observe the different aspects of our perception. We then seek clarity on what we *are* and what we *are not*. By becoming the *observer* or *enjoyer* of our sensations rather than *identifying with* the sensations, we can discern a real sense of being as opposed to linking our beingness with our sensations.

During this exercise, when I speak a line or phrase, repeat it to yourself and try to feel it in your body. This exercise is not about remembering exactly what I say but rather trying to center and open your inner awareness. Let's begin by being aware of the **world around us**.

I am aware that I am surrounded by earth, by mountains and trees, valleys and flowers, but I am not earth. I am the enjoyer of earth.

I am aware that I am surrounded by water, by streams, rivers, lakes, oceans, clouds and rain, but I am not water. I am the enjoyer of water.

I am aware that I am surrounded by air, by wind, by sky and atmosphere, but I am not air. I am the enjoyer of air.

I am aware that I am surrounded by fire, by the sun, by heat, electricity, and lightening, but I am not fire. I am the enjoyer of fire.

I am aware that I am surrounded by space, by ether, by dark matter, by infinite space, but I am not space. I am the enjoyer of space.

Now we will focus on the **Subtle Elements,** the objects of sense, which connect directly with specific senses: shapes and forms, sounds, texture, flavor, and scent.

I am aware that I am surrounded by shapes and forms, shadows and light, but I am not these shapes and forms. I am the enjoyer of shape and form.

I am aware that I am surrounded by sound waves, but I am not a sound wave. I am the enjoyer of sound.

I am aware that I am surrounded by texture, but I am not texture; I am the enjoyer of texture.

I am aware that I am surrounded by flavor, but I am not flavor. I am the enjoyer of flavor.

I am aware that I am surrounded by scents and odors, but I am not these scents and odors. I am the observer of scents and odors.

Now, we will focus on the **Organs of Action**: the mouth for speech and communication, the hands for grasping and holding, the feet for movement, the sexual organs for procreation and pleasure, the digestive system for consumption, digestion, nourishment, and elimination.

I am aware of this mouth that creates sound, but I am not this mouth. I am the enjoyer of communicating.

I am aware of these hands that grasp and hold, but I am not these hands. I am the enjoyer of grasping.

I am aware of these feet by which I move, but I am not these feet. I am the enjoyer of movement.

I am aware of these sexual organs that bring pleasure and new life, but I am not these sexual organs. I am the enjoyer of pleasure and procreation.

I am aware of this digestive system that consumes, digests, nourishes and eliminates, but I am not this digestive system. I am the enjoyer of a living body.

Now, we will focus on feeling the **Organs of Perception**: the eyes and seeing forms, the ears and hearing sounds, the skin and the sensation of touch and texture, the tongue and tasting flavors, and finally, the nose and smelling scents.

I am aware of these eyes that see, but I am not these eyes. I am the enjoyer of seeing.

I am aware of these ears that hear, but I am not these ears. I am the enjoyer of hearing.

I am aware of this skin that feels, but I am not this skin. I am the enjoyer of feeling and touching.

I am aware of this nose that smells, but I am not this nose. I am the enjoyer of smelling.

I am aware of this tongue that tastes, but I am not this tongue. I am the enjoyer of tasting.

Now we journey into the **Subtle Realms of the Mind**. All the while, we'll focus on the thought "I am" and on discriminating between "I am" and the other functions of the mind. Try variations on the statements that follow and notice what resonates with you. You only need to connect with one of these statements to enter the deeper soul consciousness.

I am aware of my sense organs merging in my brain. I am undifferentiated sensation.

I am aware of my brain. From my brain I get my sense of being. I am not my brain. I am the enjoyer of my sense of being.

From my sense of being, the first thought to arise is **"I am."**

I am aware of being surrounded by thoughts. I am not my thoughts. I am the observer of thoughts.

Within my sense of being, thoughts arise. I perceive thoughts. I am not my thoughts. I am the observer of my thinking.

Stay rooted in the idea of yourself as the observer for the rest of this exercise.

Let's emerge slowly from this meditation while remaining rooted in a deeper sense of self. During the day, make note of how easy it is to get lost in sensations, thoughts, and concerns: all the things that are not you. This technique of separating your core sense of self from all the foreign objects and sensations around you will show you peace and help you stay centered in your core self-awareness.

## Chanting Mantra and Japa

*Ten minutes*

**Teacher Note:** *Chanting selected words (mantras) is the essence of many spiritual practices. The Sanskrit word "Japa" means "the meditative repetition of a mantra." The words chanted, either aloud or silently, can be in one's native language or in a foreign language. It is important to know the meaning of the words used. Through his extensive research and book The Relaxation Response, Dr. Herbert Benson of the Mind/Body Medical Institute at Boston's Massachusetts General Hospital states that using the word "one" as a mantra is as effective as any other word.*

*The length of this exercise can vary greatly. In some parts, the humming or chanting will continue while you give further instructions.*

We will begin our exploration of chanting with humming. As you hum, you will hear many other voices in the room, but the key is to remain focused on your own humming. This brings about the meditative aspect of chanting. Be sure to enunciate enough to hear your own chant.

One of the nice things about humming is it creates time for an extra-long exhale because you are slowly and steadily releasing the exhale as you hum. This lengthened breathing helps relax the body.

To begin, simply listen to the note I hum. When you're ready to begin humming, inhale deeply, and on the exhale, join with your hum. You do not need to match my pitch exactly. We'll do this together three times.

Let's start by feeling the vibration in our throats and just relaxing into the feeling of the humming. You may think of it like a cat purring in a very relaxed state.

We will hum in unison together for the first three times. Then, please go at your own pace.

Breathe in and hum on the exhale. *[Initiate the first hum for your class.]*

This time, feel that you are creating the humming from the upper back of your throat, as if you were to pull your tongue all the way to the back of your mouth and into the nasal region. Take a breath in and hum on the exhale.

Once more... Now, pause and we'll rest for a moment.

Now, shift your awareness to your heart. Concentrate specifically on the sternum, which lies below your throat and runs down the length of your chest. This is the breastbone. Feel the vibration of your humming in the sternum.

Pause here.

For the next segment, choose either the heart, throat, or nasal area to focus on. As you focus on your chosen area, we will begin with a hum and then transition to chanting the sound "Aum." To do this, we will open our mouths and make the "ah" sound. We'll sustain the "ah" until half our breath is expelled, and then to complete the exhale we'll bring our lips together to form the sound of "mmm." Together, these utterances create the "Aum" sound, which in Sanskrit represents the cosmic power behind all of creation. These same utterances, when rearranged, can create the chants of other faiths, such as "Sha Lom," "Om," or "Amen."

First, let's hum. Draw in a deep inhale, and then exhale your hum.

On your next exhale, focus on the "ah" sound and then bring your lips together for the "m" sound. We'll do three rounds together and then go at our own pace for three to five more rounds of breath. Breathe in and exhale "Aum."

Pause here and feel the openness and release that chanting creates.

We will close this segment with a Sanskrit mantra and then an English version of it. This way, you will know what the word means and can decide which version you prefer to chant, whichever comes to you more easily. The first word is a Sanskrit word: *shanti.* The English version for *shanti* is "peace." We will chant "shanti" three times and "peace" three times.

Beginning with "shanti," draw in your inhale. "Shanti."

Next, "peace."

Now, chant three more rounds with the version you prefer: "shanti" or "peace."

Now, pause and feel the sensations the chant produced. Explore the feelings the sounds and vibrations brought you. As you acknowledge this experience, slowly bring your awareness back to your surroundings.

Chanting, like the power of music and song, can profoundly lift our spirits, our awareness, and even alter our brains. When purposefully integrated into your meditation practice, chanting and singing can give you a boost on many levels.

## Meditation on Fun

*Three to five minutes*

In this exercise, we will use the powers of imagination and visualization to focus on the fun in our lives. The ability to let loose and have fun is a skill many adults neglect to cultivate, but the experience of "fun" has benefits beyond the activity itself. Having fun energizes our bodies, inspires our minds, and lightens our hearts.

To begin, close your eyes and envision your life from a bird's-eye point of view. Envision one or two things you like to do. Likely, the first or second thing that comes to mind is one of the major sources of fun in your life. Now, pull back your scope of awareness and see your life by the month, the week, or even daily, and ask yourself how often you make time and space for your fun activity.

Scan through the experiences of your life and notice the fun moments. Perhaps ask yourself, "What are the moments I really look forward to?" "Which activities help me lighten the proverbial load I carry?" See if, right here and now, you can emulate the emotion or feeling you derive from the fun activities you're imagining. Perhaps it's relief, ease, contentment, humor, playfulness, or joy.

If you cannot identify joyful activities in your life, now is the time to visualize bringing more fun into your day. Even one small idea is enough to get you started.

## Mindful Movement and Walking Meditation

*Five to ten minutes*

**Teacher Note:** *The script below is for a walking meditation, but it can be used for any kind of movement – perhaps a gentle series of yoga poses or dance moves. Regardless of the activity, all movements are done very slowly with attention placed on each part of the movement. This is a technique for bringing mindfulness into our everyday life of motion. It is a welcome exercise for those who may not be comfortable remaining in a seated position for an extended period.*

*This script is intended to give an overall idea of what cues might be given during a mindful movement session. It is not necessary to follow this script exactly while teaching; please feel free to use your own words or to vary the movements used. Leave plenty of time in silence for students to practice mindful movement.*

"

Come to a standing position. Place the feet apart so each is directly under a hip, and spread your toes. Stand tall and relaxed. Close your eyes and bring attention to the soles of the feet. Without needing to move or change anything, notice how your weight is distributed on the soles of the feet. Become aware of any other sensations in the feet. Now, slowly move your attention up the legs, noticing any sensations. Become mindful of your whole body, its weight on the feet.

Now bring the attention to the breath. Without changing your breathing, observe your natural breath as it flows in and out through your airways. It doesn't matter if your breath is long, short, deep, or shallow. Simply be aware of each breath as it happens in the present moment.

Maintain awareness of these physical sensations as you begin to walk very slowly, taking small steps. Be mindful of your weight as it shifts from one foot to the other. Inhale as you lift one foot, and observe the sensation of lifting your foot off the earth. Exhale as you place your foot back down, and carefully observe the sensations.

If your mind wanders during the practice, simply notice it has wandered and bring your attention back to the sensation of walking. If you like, you can use a word to help you focus, for example silently repeating the verb "shifting" to yourself as the weight shifts, or "lifting" as the foot lifts, or "stepping" as you place the foot back down. As you do this, try not to use the word as an instruction but rather a simple reminder to be present with the sensations of walking.

**Teacher Note:** *Repeat the instructions periodically to help students stay focused.*

Mindfully take just two more steps, and then come to a stop. Feel the sensation of your body weight in the soles of the feet. Feel any sensations present in the body. Observe the rhythm of your breath.

**Teacher Note:** *Announce that the end of the meditation is nearing. Cue the students to take any gentle movements that may feel good before resuming their seated position for the remainder of class.*

## Loving-Kindness Meditation

*Ten to fifteen minutes*

**Teacher Note:** *Loving-kindness meditation is called "Metta" (Pali) or "Maitri" (Sanskrit). This meditation is a central practice in the Buddhist tradition.*

*In this practice, we cultivate a feeling of loving-kindness (compassion and friendliness) toward ourselves and others. A wish for happiness and well-being is directed toward oneself and others, including our loved ones, neutral people, challenging people (most difficult), and finally, to all beings.*

*Pause occasionally to allow time for your students to practice loving-kindness.*

"

Let's begin by coming into a comfortable and upright seated position. If you are seated on the floor, consider adding folded blankets under the sit bones, and feel free to lean against a wall. If you are seated on a chair, place the soles of the feet flat on the floor or on blocks if your feet don't reach the floor. Allow the hands to rest softly in the lap. Sit tall with the crown of your head lifted toward the ceiling. Your eyes can be closed or half open with an unfocused, downward gaze.

Now, bring attention to your body and notice any sensations. Gradually become increasingly aware of the neutral sensations: the weight of the body on the sit bones, the temperature of the air, the movements of the breath. No need to change your breath; rather, just observe its natural rise and fall. Let your attention be absorbed by all the sensations of the breath in the body. Feel your whole body breathing.

If thoughts are floating around in the mind, notice them. Don't try to stop or change the thoughts. Just notice them and avoid following one thought to the next. Instead, gently bring back your attention to the sensations of breath in the body. When the next thought arises, notice it and allow it to be there, but bring your attention back to the breath.

Notice whether there are any emotions present at this moment. There may be very strong emotions, or you may not feel any emotions at all. Either way, practice opening your awareness to the experience. If you have emotions, acknowledge their presence. Notice whether there are any accompanying physical sensations. Then, gently return your attention to the breath.

Now bring the attention to the area around the heart and invite the breath to move through your heart space.

Here we begin the practice of loving-kindness by making heartfelt wishes for our own wellbeing. You may use any wish that resonates with you, or you can repeat the following silently to yourself:

*May I be happy.*
*May I be healthy.*
*May I be safe.*
*May I be peaceful and at ease.*

As you repeat your wishes, open yourself to the heartfelt intention of your words in order to receive them. Notice any feelings that arise as you repeat this sincere prayer for your health and happiness.

Now, bring to mind someone who is precious to you. This may be a person or a pet, alive or passed. Let it be someone who has touched your life closely, such as a family member, respected mentor, friend, or lover. Picture this precious being and imagine how they look when they are happy and at peace. Invite the emotions that accompany this image to fill your heart. This is the feeling of loving-kindness.

As you visualize this being, offer wishes for their wellbeing:

*May you be happy.*
*May you be healthy.*
*May you be safe.*
*May you be peaceful and at ease.*

As you repeat these words, allow yourself to open to the heartfelt intention behind them. Notice any feelings that arise as you repeat this sincere prayer for the health and happiness of your loved one.

Now, bring to mind someone who is neutral to you; an acquaintance you don't have strong feelings about. Perhaps it is someone who works at a business you frequent or someone you see in your neighborhood but do not know very well. As you visualize this being, offer wishes for their wellbeing:

> *May you be happy.*
> *May you be healthy.*
> *May you be safe.*
> *May you be peaceful and at ease.*

As you repeat these words, allow yourself to open to the heartfelt intention behind them. Notice any feelings that arise as you repeat this sincere prayer for the health and happiness of your acquaintance.

Next, bring to mind someone who is challenging for you, a person for whom you have difficult feelings, perhaps someone with whom you have argued, or someone who has hurt you in the past. Note that this is the most difficult loving-kindness practice and may not always be appropriate. As you visualize this being, offer wishes for their wellbeing:

> *May you be happy.*
> *May you be healthy.*

*May you be safe.*
*May you be peaceful and at ease.*

As you repeat these words, allow yourself to open to the heartfelt intention behind them. Notice any feelings that arise as you repeat this sincere prayer for the health and happiness of the one you find challenging.

Now, send your well-wishes out in widening circles to include the entire universe of beings.

Now, release all your wishes for loving-kindness and return your attention to the present moment. Notice the sensations in your body, your breath, your thoughts, and the emotions you are experiencing.

**Teacher Note:** *Pause, and then signal the end of the meditation. Allow time for everyone's attention to come back to the room before continuing with the session.*

## Mindful Eating

*Five minutes*

**Teacher Note:** *The Mindful Eating practice is one way to integrate mindfulness into an everyday experience. It benefits the mind by promoting single-pointed concentration and focus. It also benefits the body by enhancing* *digestion through slower eating and thorough mastication. A food item such as a piece of fruit, chocolate, or a raisin can be eaten with mindfulness.*

With the piece of food placed in front of you on a small plate or napkin, notice the appearance of the food.

Notice the weight, texture, and feel of the food.

Notice the smell of the food.

Consider the factors that made it possible for you to have this food: the sun, the soil, the rain, and those who planted, cultivated, harvested, processed, and brought it to market.

Now, bite into the food while remaining aware of the sensations it possesses: the aroma, the texture, the taste, and so on.

## Concluding The Meditation

*Two to three minutes*

For the last two to three minutes of class, please recall whichever exercise brought you the most satisfaction.

As you end your meditation, come back to your surroundings. If desired, make an intention to maintain
your heightened inner awareness. The key to holding
on to a meditative feeling is to link the calmness you
are feeling to your slow and relaxed breath.

Now, begin to slowly open your eyes while keeping
your awareness on your breath.

## PART 5: ASSIMILATION AND MANIFESTATION

### Assimilation Exercise

**Teacher Note:** *Time permitting, you can invite the students
to do some journaling or other form of self-expression to
assimilate or integrate their experience of meditation
into their day-to-day lives. They may appreciate the opportunity to record inspiration or insights gleaned from
the meditative experience, even by typing them into their
phones or using scrap pieces of paper.*

## ENDING CLASS AND NEXT STEPS

**Teacher Note:** *Your final words to the class will leave a
strong impression. Here is a list of suggestions for how to
end your class.*

◆ Sing or chant with or without instrumental
   accompaniment.

- ◆ If there are fewer than ten guests, ask them to share their names and the quality they chose to focus on during the visualization exercise. Don't forget to share yours!

- ◆ Offer a brief, inspirational reading or quotation.

- ◆ Offer suggestions for how to continue the practice on their own.

- ◆ Suggest next steps for their meditation journey.

*If your intention is to stay in touch with the members of your audience, then be sure to gather their contact information and leave your contact information with them.*

# CHAPTER 8

# The Science of Meditation

Here you will find a brief description of the science and physiology behind stress and its powerful antidote: meditation. The main points may be more than enough for most audiences. That said, you may use this information to springboard further into the science behind meditation, which may influence and provide inspiration for your teaching.

## THE AUTONOMIC NERVOUS SYSTEM AND THE BODY'S STRESS RESPONSE

Mammals first appeared 175 million years ago, primates sixty-five million years ago, and early humans seven million years ago. It is estimated that *Homo sapiens*, our modern human species, first appeared 200,000 years ago. We battled for our lives against giant birds, crocodiles, leopards, grizzly bears, saber-toothed tigers, snakes, hyenas, Komodo dragons, and great apes.

The human body we inhabit is an ancient biological system that has evolved out of our efforts to survive. As a result, our nervous system is highly responsive to stress.

## MODERN STRESS

Today, we create and partake in a society that no longer unwinds and relaxes. For example, our engagement with mass media—the 24-hour news cycle, television, the internet, social media—engenders a feeling of "always on." This constant activity will be, if not carefully and consciously controlled, a harbinger of diseases rooted in stress.

Our nervous systems respond to all forms of stress, whether mental, physical, real, or imagined. Stressful situations, whether time-bound—such as looming work deadlines and traffic jams—or chronic—such as persistent worry about social standing or financial difficulties—can trigger cascades of stress hormones. Over time, repeated activation of the stress response takes a toll on our physical and psychological health.

Even low-level stress, if chronic, keeps the body's stress response activated, much like a motor that idles when it should be turned off. Research shows that this type of stress contributes to high blood pressure, promotes the formation of artery-clogging deposits, and causes brain changes that may contribute to anxiety, depression, and addiction.

Research also indicates that chronic stress may contribute to obesity through both direct mechanisms (eating more) and indirect mechanisms (decreased sleep and exercise).

## UNDERSTANDING OUR NERVOUS SYSTEM

The activity of our bodies is regulated, both consciously and unconsciously, by the nervous system. The two main parts of the nervous system are the central nervous system, which is composed of the brain and spinal cord, and the peripheral nervous system, which is composed of all the nerves that connect the central nervous system to the other parts of the body.

The three subsystems in our peripheral nervous system are:

**1.** The somatic, which mediates conscious movement and allows us to exercise at least partial control over some of our bodily functions. These include the movements of our head, arms, legs, or other body parts, as well as the function of some internal organs, such as the bowels and bladder.

**2.** The enteric, which regulates our gastrointestinal tract.

**3.** The autonomic, which controls systems that are largely unconscious. There are two main aspects of the autonomic nervous system relevant to the science of meditation:

**a.** The sympathetic nervous system, which controls our fight, flight, and freeze responses

**b.** The parasympathetic nervous system, which controls our rest and digest responses

Evolutionarily, our two foundational modes of being are activity and rest. Activity mode includes the fight, flight, and freeze responses, and rest mode includes digestion, repose, and sleep. We react to physical and psychological threats by fighting, fleeing, or freezing, and once the threat is gone, we recover by resting and digesting.

The autonomic nervous system evolved as a survival mechanism, enabling us to react quickly to life-threatening situations. This system regulates processes in the body that we usually don't notice or control consciously, such as our heart rate and metabolism. Breathing, too, is usually managed involuntarily, but we can choose to consciously control our breathing. *Enter the power of meditation.* Breath control is one of the keys to successful meditation.

The primary concern for residents of the modern, developed world is psychological stress. When danger is perceived, the sympathetic nervous system activates the body into a fight, flight, or freeze response. It provides a burst of energy and tells the body to get ready for physical and mental activity. It causes the heart to beat harder and faster, and it opens the airways for easy breathing. It also temporarily stops digestion so the body can focus on immediate physical movement.

When the threat has passed, the parasympathetic nervous system takes over and allows the body to calm down, rest, and digest. It also restores homeostasis and remains active during the body's recuperation period. This system causes a decrease in heart rate, stimulates smooth muscle movement of the intestines, and activates the secretion of saliva, digestive juices and tissue-building hormones.

Every stress moment needs an equal rest moment. If we don't have that balance, we lose our equilibrium both physically and psychologically. Our modern lives are so full of stress, real and imagined, that our nervous systems are out of balance. If we do not properly disengage or re-cover from the stress in our lives, then our nervous systems will struggle to return to equilibrium.

Thousands of years of evolution have resulted in a finely tuned nervous system. To be healthy, we must respect the natural workings of this system and find ways to nur-ture balance and ease in our bodies. We cannot submit ourselves to constant stress and stimulation and expect to remain in good health. We need to rest and digest. Meditation helps with this rebalancing.

## HOW TO ACTIVATE THE PARASYMPATHETIC NERVOUS SYSTEM

The task we face is to temper the activity of the sympa-thetic nervous system with that of the parasympathetic nervous system. All the meditation practices taught in this book do exactly that. Additionally, there are simple activ-ities we can build into our daily routines that foster relax-ation. I've listed several examples below.

As you try some of these, observe how the results come quickly. Your nervous system wants to switch gears and will react almost immediately.

- ♦ The very act of choosing to sit still, even just for one complete breath cycle, calms the mind and body.

- ♦ Slow, rhythmic breathing exercises are plentiful in this book and signal to the body that all dangers have passed, and it is time to rest and recover.

- ♦ Mild exercises containing an element of tranquility also cause rest and digest, such as gentle yoga or tai chi. A pleasant ten-minute walk after a meal is another tried-and-true method.

- ♦ Singing, humming, and chanting stimulate the vocal cords and facilitate long, slow exhalation, which signals to the body that it is time to relax. Take the example of church attendees who sing and hum together to foster communion with the divine and to elevate the spirit in a relaxed, harmonized manner.

- ♦ Engage in prosody, i.e., the act of speaking slowly, rhythmically, and melodically, as when reading poetry or telling stories.

- ♦ The very act of laughing out loud (even if there is nothing to laugh at) will prompt the release of tension. Watch a funny movie or read a joke book and be silly enough to laugh out loud, and you will soon feel the benefits.

♦ Interestingly, cold water also triggers relaxation. This can be achieved by splashing cold water on your face, drinking a cold beverage and letting your tongue be immersed in it before swallowing, or a cold shower; even a minute of cold at the end of your hot shower does the trick.

Various studies demonstrate the cognitive changes that can occur through the practice of meditation. Neuro-imaging technology has shown that meditation can result in alterations of neural circuitry and other physical structures of the brain. The effects of meditation can also be seen in brainwave activity.

Combining a basic understanding of the science behind mediation with a knowledge of meditation techniques is a sturdy foundation upon which to begin your teaching endeavors. The experience of sharing meditation with others has been one of the great joys of my life, and I have so enjoyed sharing my tried and tested methods with you here.

Now it's time for you to go share!

P. blishing, 1991

# ADDITIONAL READING

My hope is that this book has provided you with the essentials to begin sharing meditation with others, but I have touched on a wide variety of topics that may warrant further reading and study, depending on your interests. For this reason, I have included the below list of resources.

Babbit, Irving. *The Dhammapada*. New York: Oxford University Press, 1936.

Bandler, Richard. *Using Your Brain—for a Change*. Moab: Real People Press, 1985.

Benson, Herbert. *The Relaxation Response*. New York: William Morrow, 1975.

Brown, Brian. *The Wisdom of the Chinese: Their Philosophy in Sayings and Proverbs*. New York: Garden City Publishing Co., Inc., 1920.

Gawain, Shakti. *Creative Visualizations: Use the Power of Your Imagination to Create What You Want in Your Life*. Novato: New World Library, 1978.

Lao Tzu. *Tao Teh Ching*. Translated by Dr. John C. H. Wu. New York: St. John's University Press, 1961.

McKeever, Sujantra. *Learn to Meditate*. San Diego: McKeever Publishing, 1994.

McKeever, Sujantra. *Paths are Many, Truth is One: Exploring the Unity of All Religions*. San Diego: McKeever Publishing, 1998.

McKeever, Sujantra. *Strategy for Success: An Outline for Personal Growth*. San Diego: McKeever Publishing, 1993.

Müller, F. Max. *The Upanishads*. New York: Dover Publications, 1962.

Prabhavananda, Swami and Christopher Isherwood. *Bhagavad-Gita: The Song of God*. New York: Signet Classic, 2002.

Prabhavananda, Swami and Frederick Manchester. *The Upanishads: Breath of the Eternal*. New York: Signet Classic, 2002.

In addition to the books listed above, authors and spiritual figures I find instructive and inspiring are Sri Aurobindo, Sri Chinmoy, Sri Ramakrishna, Ramana Maharshi, Swami Vivekananda, Loren Eiseley, Ralph Waldo Emerson, Henry David Thoreau, René Descartes, Immanuel Kant, Sigmund Freud, Carl Jung, Abraham Maslow, and Joseph Campbell.

Recommendations aside, you will do well to follow your own interests, inspirations, and inner guidance. Your life experiences and inner wisdom will carry you far as a meditation instructor. May your journey be filled with happiness, health, and peace.

Made in the USA
Middletown, DE
14 August 2021

46082431R00073